Contents

UNIVERSITY OF
GLOUCESTERSHIRE
at Cheltenham and Gloucester

COMMUNICATIONS and NETWORKS

a handbook for the first-time user
<u>2nd Edition</u>

06

Phil Croucher

Published by
Sigma Press, 1 South Oak Lane, Wilmslow, Cheshire SK9 6AR, England.

British Library Cataloguing in Publication Data
A CIP record for this book is available from the British Library.

ISBN: 1-85058-534-2

Printed by: Manchester Free Press

Preface

This book is for people who would like to extend the use of their computers, possibly for teleworking, or have been designated the "Company Expert", and need to get to grips with the subject of Communications and Networks quickly.

Unfortunately, both topics can be highly technical but, with any luck, you should find the following pages easy to read yet informative – the intention being to provide a book for the intelligent beginner that may be read on the train or bus, for instance, but still provide an adequate level of knowledge to be useful, or at least point to where further knowledge can be found if it's needed.

The idea is to give a general view of a wide area before you launch off into areas that interest you most. There will be a slant towards the IBM and its compatibles because they are the most commonly used computers in business, but communications is communications and other products will be mentioned where the principles don't change.

The nature of the subject also means that it's impossible to keep jargon out in the early stages; words may appear from nowhere with little explanation. You will find most of these in the glossary at the back of the book – they're there because in many cases it was felt that too many explanations at the time would spoil the flow of the text, or that nowhere else could be found to put them – Appendix A, *Instant Netware*, is where it is for the same reason!

Phil Croucher

1

Communications

Much of modern life would grind to a halt if computers couldn't talk to each other; this is done mostly over telephone lines, but sometimes they are joined directly, such as when you exchange data between a desktop computer and a laptop.

Over the telephone, you can book theatre and airline tickets, check your bank statement, the weather, railway timetables or simply connect to a *Bulletin Board* or *On-Line Service* to pass messages to other people. Alternatively, you could keep in touch with the office from home, with *Electronic Mail*, or E-mail for short.

Electronic Mail is the nearest we have yet to the paperless office—you could think of it as space-age telex. It just means the sending of letters over cables rather than in envelopes, directly to computers in the same building, or over the telephone system.

A Bulletin Board is a computer that is permanently switched on and connected to the telephone line, programmed to answer calls automatically. It acts as an electronic noticeboard, where anyone can "pin up" notices that others who care to *log on* can read, or where people can have electronic conversations between themselves. Some companies use Bulletin Boards to handle orders or make information available to the general public, but there are hundreds of private ones run by enthusiasts, all free of charge.

An On-Line Service is what you might call a commercial Bulletin Board; it performs the same function, but is open to anyone who pays its charges. You get a personal "mailbox" and access to vast amounts of knowledge from *information providers*, who are in it for the money. The information can range from stocks and shares to train times.

Electronic Mail has also made exchanging data between dissimilar computers less of a problem—you just *upload* the data to an electronic mailbox where it's stored until needed. When the message is *downloaded* by the intended recipient it's automatically converted to the format their computer requires.

This is OK if you only do it occasionally, but a large company with a factory full of PCs and a few mainframes may want something more convenient. If the transfers are done often and the links required are likely to be permanent, the equipment will be better off in a *network*, of which more in Chapter 15.

There are some disadvantages to all this, of course. One is that your co-respondent must also be using the system, and another is that you generally have to pay for it, but all the above variations boil down to one thing in the end, which is making one computer talk to another.

Potted History

The first real communications systems were telegraphs using heavy copper wires, built around the 1840s. Electrical signals weaken the further they travel, so the wires were split up into manageable sections, and human beings used as repeaters, taking in and retransmitting the messages every hundred miles or so (in those days, of course, labour was cheaper than the equipment). The Morse Code was also developed at this time.

Eventually, ways were sought to send data mechanically (the operators were probably getting tired by this time), for which Morse Code wasn't suitable because of the varying lengths of the dots and dashes it was made of, so a Frenchman, Emile Baudot, invented the *Baudot code* in the 1870s which used marks and spaces of equal duration on paper tape to represent characters.

Life thus became easier for the operators as they began to use paper tape for receiving and transmitting; all they had to do was move the paper between the encoders and decoders on their desks.

The Baudot Code paved the way for the teleprinter, which is nothing more nor less than a long-range typewriter, but the Code's restriction of 5 marks and spaces per character meant that only 32 possible combinations of them could be used, which was not enough to cater for the alphabet and all the numbers and punctuation marks needed for everyday conversation.

This was solved by using the LETTER SHIFT and FIGURE SHIFT keys on the keyboard, which multiplied this by nearly twice – after either of these keys were pressed, the codes following it were treated as figures or letters until the key was pressed again.

Teleprinters were slow and cumbersome for many reasons, including slack in mechanical linkages, starting and stopping of electrical motors and engagement and disengagement of clutches as each character was transmitted, which meant their maximum speed was between 30-70 characters a second. Obviously, these speeds are too low for computers, or they'd start getting bored and cause trouble!

In due course, the march of technology replaced the marks on paper with holes, which allowed switches to make electrical connections through them.

The teleprinter network eventually became the telex system and was the origin of many of the signalling standards now used for communications between computers.

Common Ground

In the early days, several types of computers and ways of communicating between them had been established, but the designs were kept behind the various manufacturers' doors so there was little likelihood of cross-connection with anything else.

As a result, these were known as *closed systems*, and one significant drawback of them (to you, anyway) was that you were locked into buying one particular brand, regardless of whether it suited your needs or not.

Naturally enough, manufacturers loved the idea, but in 1977 the *International Standards Organisation* (ISO) undertook to lay down standards which eventually (in 1983) took the form of a sort of dictionary that defined *Open* (as opposed to closed) *Systems Interconnection*, otherwise known as OSI.

This was so that manufacturers would be encouraged to make sure that people could connect their systems to others easily.

It did this by describing an architecture for data communications systems (that is, what is intended to happen when computers talk to each other) in words of very much more than one syllable. It can be likened to a philosophy of communications which ensures that the interconnection of everything is as easy as possible. It's based on the thinking that communications can be broken down into several hierarchical layers, a bit like the chart that shows how each part of a company interacts with each other.

You know what happens — although The Chairman can talk to his equal in another company, internally he delegates tasks to executives which are sub-delegated down the line until you're the one that ends up doing everything, passing the results on to the other company where your opposite number passes them back up their system in the same way as they came down in yours (see diagram overleaf).

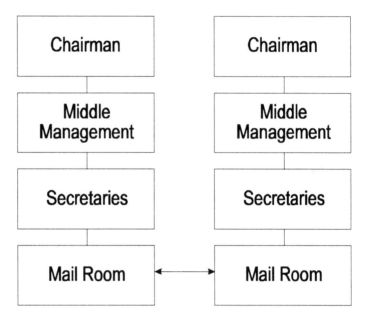

The real problems arise when the Chairman of one is a different nationality to the other and further complicates things by not speaking his language! Translators are therefore needed to convert from one to the other.

Data communication is similar. At the top, the program in one computer talks to its equal in another (e.g. Chairman to Chairman). They agree on what they're going to send, how, when and at what speed. The data itself is passed down to the Mail Room (i.e. you) through several levels, having been suitably prepared and converted at each stage, whereupon it's sent along the chosen channel to the next machine and the reverse procedure happens.

The reason that things need to happen this way is because manufacturers are still allowed some discretion as to how they make things — after all, if they had to stick to too rigid a standard, there would be no variety at all, and we all know how bad things can be when they're designed by committee.

Thus, there's a need to ensure (at the bottom levels at least) that everything is in a standard form. The translation of the character set (or alphabet) used in one system to that of the other is done through *interfaces*, which occupy the same position as the translators mentioned previously — that is, they convert from one language to another. They are not identifiable pieces of equipment, though; properly, they are *boundaries* to which pieces of equipment can be attached and across which communications take place.

On the other hand, the discussions between the systems (about what they're going to do (at equal levels) is done with equipment of similar standing and with like operating procedures – this is also known as using *protocol*, and further described much later on.

Just to try and make the above clearer – an interface is a connection point between two *dissimilar* pieces of equipment that may use different character sets and possibly different ways of transmitting.

A protocol, on the other hand, is a set of rules (usually embodied in software) that regulate the interactions between machines or processes that are *alike* or have similar functions.

The OSI Model

The *OSI model* is a map of the communication process, the idea being that if you had a piece of equipment, you could find its location on the model and deduce its relationship to everything else. It's actually quite boring and, although it is useful knowledge, you won't miss much if you skip the rest of this chapter.

According to OSI, there are seven layers in the communications process, with things getting more and more sophisticated as you progress upwards.

Each layer is dependent on (and communicates only with) the ones diZ @0 bove or beneath, and there is a defined interface between them which is made as flexible as possible so that designers can vary things within the standard; in other words, the standard defines *what* is to be done, whilst leaving it to designers as to *how*.

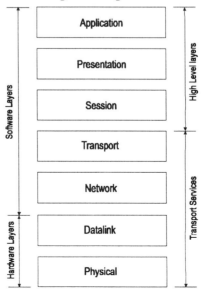

The real world isn't so tidy, though, and (just to make things awkward) it's possible that some levels may be mixed in many products, or even missed out altogether. Some popular protocols (e.g. TCP/IP – see Chapter 20) don't fit in into the model at all!

The lower 3 were originally proposed by a European standards group, the *International Telegraph and Telephone Consultative Committee* (CCITT), which was part of the International Telecommunications Union, an agency of the United Nations. It has now been replaced by the *International Telecommunications Union - Telecommunications*, or ITU-T.

Their intention was to promote some sort of commonality between equipment, and their ideas were later adopted in the OSI proposals. The British Standards Institute also had a hand in it somewhere.

However, CCITT (not to be outdone) laid down even more specifications within OSI, notably the V and X series of trahnsmission standards. For example, the X.25 standards are used to define *digital packet* transmission standards, and V.24 covers *analogue* equipment used on the telephone lines, but you will find all these discussed more fully later.

In General

The first two layers are known collectively as the *hardware layers*, as they provide the solid foundation on which everything else is built (equipment layout, transmission speeds, etc).

The next five tend to relate to systems software and procedures, so you could compare them to the first two in the same way that white collar workers are related to blue collar ones in a factory.

They are more closely tied to the functional characteristics of terminals and application software, and are more theoretical than technical. They enable you to think of things in more abstract terms, like referring to devices by name rather than by a series of addresses, so software can be written that will run on any communications installation built in accordance with the standards.

Because the bottom four levels have to do with the manipulation of data, they are also sometimes (as a group) referred to as the *transport services*; as such they would include "middle management", whose job it is to see that the orders of Those On High are carried out. Similarly, the remaining levels are also called the *high-level layers* and concern themselves with the meaning of the data transported – rather like laying down management policy in a company.

They can be said to make use of the transport layers. The unit of exchange in them all is the *message*.

The Physical Layer

Starting at the bottom, the physical layer concerns itself with the type of connections between devices, including the mechanical and electrical aspects (that is, connectors, cabling, voltages and their functions). As it also covers equipment using the telephone system, a good example is V.24, mentioned above, which goes into such fine detail as what voltages appear at what times and for how long on what pins of particular connectors.

However, it doesn't go so far as to define where the voltages come from — that's left up to the manufacturers. Provided the specifications are interpreted correctly, though, there should be few problems, even if a few liberties are taken in the design stages.

It's the most error-prone area and the unit of exchange between everything is the *bit* (you will find more about physical links later, and more about bits in the next chapter). If you think in terms of a railway, it's the equivalent of the tracks.

The Data-link Layer

This layer deals with the meaningful transmission of the information as it travels around the tracks — i.e. how data is encoded and decoded as it's sent and received around the system, including the framing, addressing and error checking of messages; the unit of exchange in this case is the *frame*, which is a group of data bits, with a *flag* at each end to indicate its beginning and ending. It's similar to collecting carriages together to make up a train — this level assembles everything and sends the train on its way, checking the carriages as they go.

In telephone terms, it's whether the noises you hear are the same as those that were sent. A system called HDLC (amongst others, such as *Advanced Data Communications and Control Procedures* — ADCCP or *Bisync*), which does this for you, comes under this heading.

The Data Link layer can be split into:

- The **Media Access Layer**, which specifies the protocol.

- The **Logical Link Control**, which defines how messages are segmented into frames.

The Network Layer

The network layer is the third one up, controlling the movement of data from point to point, sometimes including verification of receipt, etc. (but this may also be done by level 2). It's like the traffic police or, in other words, whether your telephone noises are the ones intended for your ears or not (this layer is sometimes not used in a simple system when it's obvious where the messages go). The unit of exchange is the *packet*, which is where the X.25 standards (for packet transmission) start to be relevant.

Whereas a telephone system expects a permanent connection, packet systems don't, as data transmission (as opposed to voice) can accept a slight delay here and there, due to the lack of need for immediate feedback. Messages are split into parts (packets) that are left to get to their destination as and when they can and reassembled in the right order when they get there. Packet switching is the basis behind most data communications systems and is extensively used on networks. See Chapter 7 for more about this.

The Transport Layer

Level 4 does the same job as level 1, but between larger entities, such as groups of several computers linked together, where the unit of exchange would be the *message* (if the lower levels assemble the train, level 4 is the man in charge of the freight yard).

It lays down how connections can be made or unmade, giving the higher layers the impression of permanent transmission channels without them worrying about the details of how the data they are sending gets around.

It bridges the gap between services available and services desired, and is also where compatibility becomes crucial if you want to mix and match third party hard- and software.

The Session Layer

The Session Layer concerns itself with the management of re- sources — it allows the transfer of messages without the need to utilise all of the facilities available; in addition, it gives the most cost-effective use of everything by controlling who may send at any time (sometimes this is done by the issue of tokens, or "tickets to ride" on the system), and is the first layer where applications really begin to use names rather than numbers to keep in touch with everything. This level figuratively opens up the carriages and checks what's inside, behaving in every respect like a ticket inspector.

The Presentation Layer

Common translation facilities are provided here for the interpretation of information and the methods by which applications software can enter the network. As it deals with how things are presented, all the pretty pictures, menus and special effects on screen belong here.

The Application Layer

The highest level, where you interact with everything that the OSI model defines. It's where delivery of the communication product is finally made, including the program that gives you control without having to understand the whole process. You use it to set up and operate the other layers.

Problems

The full OSI model is still not fully defined, years after it was first proposed. New ideas (and names) are being added continually as the goalposts keep shifting (because it's designed by committee, it can be quite cumbersome).

Apart from that, just because a product conforms to OSI standards, it doesn't mean to say that it's compatible with anything on the same level. To overcome this, further specifications within each level have been made, and other models intended to streamline communications in better ways include IBM's Systems Network Architecture (SNA) and DEC's DEC Network Architecture (DNA), both of which came before OSI but are being adjusted to compensate for any differences.

Other ideas include LU 6.2 from IBM, and MAP and TOP from General Motors and Boeing, respectively (these last two are significant in their development by users rather than designers or manufacturers. Maybe they got fed up with having to sort out the choices that were available to them). Another one is ONA, or Open Network Architecture, which is British Telecom's contribution.

But so much for theory—let's get down to practicalities.

NOTES

Communications — A Closer Look

Every part of a computer communicates — the keyboard talks to the Central Processor, which in turn talks to the screen and other components inside, and the computer as a whole will talk to a printer, plotter or even another computer. This external communication between individual machines will be the basis of this book.

That done by single users can go from one extreme to the other, either linking two machines together on the same desk, or using the telephone system to get to the variety of services available all over the world. The former situation is known as *local*, and the latter *remote*, communications.

The first problem is knowing where to start. Obviously, some kind of connection is required and traffic along this will need to be controlled but, going further back, we come across the signal itself, which is what the traffic's made of in the first place.

The Signal

You are no doubt aware by now that computers use *bits* to convey information, the word **bit** being made up from the first and last letters of *bi*nary dig*it*.

The bit takes the form of a signal that can be either on or off, which is particularly useful as the computer itself operates on the binary system, using only two characters, 1 or 0, to convey meaning — you can see how they dovetail nicely. It's no coincidence that electrical appliances use the figures 1 and 0 for *On* and *Off*.

ASCII

On a PC, eight bits make a *byte*, which is equivalent to a character on the screen, as a result of which the number of data bits used to make up a character is often called the *Word Length* — 7 or 8 data bits as a group are also referred to as ASCII 7 or ASCII 8 (for IBM PCs, but the word length actually depends on the computer and programming language you're using).

ASCII (pronounced "askey", as in Arthur) is short for *American Standard Code for Information Interchange*, an internationally agreed standard (laid down by the *American National Standards Institute* – ANSI) which gives each character of the alphabet a number, translated by other equipment according to what country it thinks it's in. For example, the £ character is allocated the ASCII number 156.

"Traditional ASCII" defined 128 characters, and only 7 bits were used for each one. *Extended ASCII* kept the original 128 and added 128 more, using up the eighth bit.

Because it is a common standard, the ASCII code has become useful as a bridge between programs that want to exchange information.

Analogue vs Digital

The *digital* on-off signals that a computer generates as bits arise from switches (i.e. transistors) making and breaking contact several million times a second, forming electrical pulses in the shape of *square waves*, which have a very sharp rise as the connection is made, a plateau as the switch is held on and a sharp fall as the contact breaks.

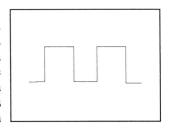

An *On* condition is recognised once the pulse reaches a certain threshold, and *Off* when it drops below it. As further protection against spurious signals, the computer will only recognise signals of a certain duration.

An *analogue* signal, on the other hand, is *analogous* to whatever it represents, and relatively smooth; the voltage over a telephone line, for instance, will rise and fall in sympathy with the loudness of your voice – the fluctuating size of the signal is what's actually measured. Compare this with a digital signal, which is noticeably jerky, and similar to tapping on a pipe to get a message through rather than using the flow of material through it. However, measuring 0s or 1s is considerably easier than measuring voltages (the word *analogue*, by the way, is often taken to mean "non-digital").

Different signals use different frequencies; for instance, as far as the authorities are concerned, speech lies between 300-3000 *cycles per second* (or *Hertz*, as it's known in the trade; it just means that the human voice is considered to vibrate within that range).

Although the full range can be anywhere between 100-1100 Hz, anything outside the official one of 300-3000 Hz is ignored, because the equipment required to detect the full spectrum of voice and hearing (your ears can detect sound between 20-20,000 Hz) would be expensive, so they make do with the defined range mentioned above. It works well, because the bulk of the power in a voice is inside this area anyway; the fact that some of the frequencies comprising it are missing accounts for telephone voices sounding tinny sometimes.

As it happens, signals used inside computers are outside the voice range described above (a square wave needs to start at 0 Hz) and we shall see how they talk to the outside world despite this when we look at telephone systems and connections to it later.

Some signals are better for certain purposes — medium wave is good enough to carry voice and music, for example, because they don't have to occupy much space, but higher grade carriers are needed for television signals, due to the amount of information in them (TV signals need to occupy the same space as a thousand voice channels).

Bandwidth

Like a road, whatever you transmit over must be "wide" enough to carry the traffic you intend to send over it. The "width" of any signal is known as its *bandwidth*; for example, voice signals, as we know, occupy 2700 Hz, or 2.7 KHz, which is 3000 minus 300 (the upper and lower limits are known as *cutoff frequencies*).

A transmission medium will also have a bandwidth, and here, the term is twisted slightly to mean the width it is *able to provide*, rather than the width it occupies. The aim, when matching signals to media, is to ensure that the signal bandwidth does not exceed that of the intended link, or that your car is not too wide for the road.

So officially, the bandwidth is the difference between the highest and the lowest range of frequencies that *a signal occupies*. Unofficially (and more commonly), it defines the amount of information that can be *carried by any media*, or signal, (that is, capacity) in a given time.

Any restrictions on bandwidth arise from the physical properties of the medium or the deliberate minimising of interference from other sources. For example, cable TV will use a 6 MHz channel in which to carry a 4.5 MHz signal, although where cables are concerned, the restrictions are more to do with the characteristics of the wires themselves; sending data too fast can change the nature of the signals and hence the information sent.

Transmission Media

Signals can be carried over anything, for example microwaves, which radiate their energies freely into space unless some sort of waveguiding is used. A *waveguide* is a hollow metal conductor which guides Ultra High Frequency radio waves in a particular direction (in other words you send them down a tube). Not only does the waveguide concentrate energy, it also reduces unwanted interference.

Other systems use *bounded media*, which perform all of the functions of a waveguide, the most common of which would be either coaxial or twisted pairs of cable, or fibreoptics.

Twisted Pairs

Early telegraph systems used the earth itself for a signal return path,

but signal losses induced by weather (especially lightning) prompted separate wires for sending and returning, so you ended up with two.

It was found later that twisting one wire with another tended to cancel out certain types of interference, which is where the name comes from. The end result looks a lot tidier than the name implies – the wiring is usually terminated in phone connectors (American-style RJ45) and plugged into telephone-type sockets (not a good idea to confuse them).

On a telephone system, twisted pairs are found on local lines, that is, from your home to the exchange, otherwise the country would be swamped with wires – trunk connections (i.e. big ones between major exchanges) are made with equipment having a much larger bandwidth to take the extra traffic, which is combined along it (see *Multiplexing* in Chapter 3).

Twisted pair cabling is easily bent around corners, and the bandwidth allows a reasonable rate of data transfer, but there are sound reasons as to why it has speed limitations.

Every electric current has an associated magnetic field, which will rise and fall in sympathy with the current flow. If current tries to move too fast down a wire, then the electromagnetic radiations from it will interfere with sensitive equipment nearby. It will also induce a current in the next wire, which will be mistaken for pulses and therefore genuine data (this is known as *crosstalk*).

The speed of data transmission along twisted pairs is kept low to stop these problems occurring. Coaxial cables don't suffer from them, as they have proper screening. Fibreoptics, of course, only use light.

However, little protection is provided from outside interference and twisted pairs can, in fact, act as receiving as well as transmitting aerials, unless shielding is used to counteract this.

Having said all that, transmission speeds have been upgraded to those associated with coaxial systems, namely around 10 Megabits per second.

Coax

Coaxial cable works on the same principle as twisted pair, except that the second wire is converted into braid and placed around the central one to act as a *screen*, which is more effective at keeping out interference. Coax needs to be handled carefully as, when it's crushed, it loses some of its screening ability. You will recognise it as that used to connect your TV to its aerial, but computer coax is made of better quality:

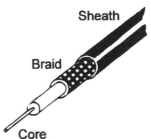

Fibreoptics

Light rays bend, or refract, when they pass from one medium to another, which is caused by the slowing down of the rays at one edge of the beam at the crossover point, which is why anything under water appears to be displaced when viewed from outside.

Because of refraction, light can reflect internally along a glass fibre and bounce along the inside (like stones skimming on the surface of the sea), giving the signals a longer effective range.

Every optic fibre (which is about the size of a human hair) consists of three strands, each inside the other.

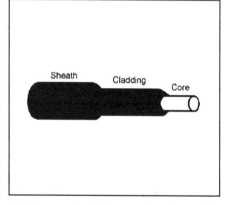

The centre one (the core) is a special low loss grade of material that has a constant *refractive index*; that is, its ability to bounce light along its inside doesn't reduce along its length. The next one (the cladding) and the outer one (the sheath) each have progressively lower refractive indexes (or is it indices?) which stop the light straying from the centre.

As transmissions are unaffected by electrical interference and don't weaken so quickly, fibreoptics are popular for long distances, especially as the transmission speeds are those of light itself (systems have been demonstrated that are capable of carrying over 4000 voice circuits per fibre and transmitting at rates in excess of 4 million bits per second over stage lengths of at least 100 km without repeaters).

Repeaters are needed, not because of *attenuation* (or weakening), but because the signal tends to get less concentrated, and spreads out. In fact, any loss of signal strength in fibres is due to:

- **Scattering** because of imperfections in the material, which can never be eliminated completely.

- **Absorption losses**, which occur when the angle of entry of the light into the fibre is larger than needed for proper refraction, whereupon the power it contains is used for digging itself into the coating rather than skimming along the insides.

- **Connection and bending losses,** which occur when the cable is not aligned properly; the ends of the fibres must be parallel to within one degree or less, otherwise the light rays will not be started properly. The core must also be as concentric with the cladding as possible.

Some advantages of using fibreoptics over other methods include:

- **Less maintenance,** because it isn't as fussy over its environment, so it doesn't need to be so watertight.

- **Noise immunity,** where external electromagnetic and radio fields don't interfere with the optical signals in the cable, and *vice versa*.

- **Security.** Optical signals in the cable can't be tapped by electromagnetic means.

- **Bandwidth** is high for its cost; the full availability is 25,000 GHz; one fibre could theoretically carry all the phone calls in USA at peak time, all at the same time.

- **High speed** over long distances.

- **Light weight.**

There is a plot to broadcast data as light signals over fibreoptic cables everywhere (similar to radio) and have your computer tuned to the particular frequency, or colour, of the data you require; this has become known as the *information superhighway*.

Disadvantages

As a vast investment has already taken place for present equipment, fibreoptics are only being installed as new plant is required (such as most new cable TV and associated telephone installations).

Every time light is split, the frequency is halved, so you need light amplifiers at all junctions. Electrical facilities are still therefore required to amplify and switch the signals, using photodiodes to convert them from light to electrical ones, switching, rearranging and generally interfering with them until they are reconverted with an LED or laser.

The main point is that once data travelling at high speed hits an electronic switching device, you get a bottleneck.

NOTES

Types of Communication

There are two types of signal traffic; *low volume*, and *interactive*, where you might control another computer from your keyboard, and *high volume*, where you just transfer data from point to point, with no need for feedback. The former would tend to come and go in short bursts, and the latter, more predictably, in a continuous stream.

Luckily, there are only two ways of sending either; eight at a time at a given signal, down eight wires at once (rather like a horse race), or one after the other down a single cable. The first method is known as *parallel* communications and the second *serial*. Each has its own pros and cons, but the most common for our purposes is serial, so let's dispose of the other first.

Parallel

Parallel communications are used over very short distances; typically inside the computer itself and to printers.

This method, together with the connector (see below), was developed by *Centronics* and used by IBM in its first PC. As a result, it has become relatively standardised. It is fast-ish, and distance-limited. The original design was one way only, but *bi-directional ports* have been developed, a side benefit of which is the ability to control the printer directly with suitable software. *Enhanced parallel ports* turn the parallel port into a high speed data bus and can transfer data at ten times the speed of standard ones. This makes them useful for attaching tape streamers or extra hard drives.

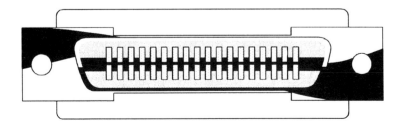

The wires are very close together, and because the strength of any signal diminishes the further it goes down the line (due to the work it has to do to get past the resistance of the wire itself), there is a chance that they could be interfered with when they become weak enough, giving the possibility of *crosstalk*, on top of normal attenuation, where data from one wire will be reflected in the next. This is why parallel communications are generally restricted to short distances unless boosters are used.

Just to send the data, we need a minimum of eight wires, so that a complete character can be sent at a time. However, that's not all. What if the receiving computer wasn't able to take everything at once (perhaps because it ran out of memory) or detected an error and wanted to tell the sender to stop and send that last bit again?

There will be other connections between the computers with another conversation going on, telling each other when to stop and start sending and giving themselves progress reports. As you can imagine, we now begin to collect quite a few wires, usually about 15 in all, dependent on the make of equipment.

As the most common encounter with parallel transmission is with printers, we will take an example of how characters are sent to one as a more detailed illustration of what goes on. However, it's also possible to make computers communicate in the same way, as when transferring data between machines, or linking to a network.

The parallel port is actually controlled by two chips, one for information and the other for control signals. Both are linked to a decoder which sorts out to which pins in the connector the relevant bits are sent.

When the printer is *on line*, it sends a *Ready* signal to the computer, whose response is *Initialisation*, sent on another wire, which clears the *buffer* (a little bit of memory which stores data so it can be sorted out before being printed).

Once the printer is initialised, the data is lined up, one bit per wire (like the start of a race) and, assuming the printer hasn't sent a *Busy* signal, a low voltage signal (*DataStrobe*) is sent to the printer. This acts like a starting gun to send the data down the lines, at the other end of which it assembles in the buffer ready for printing, after it's had a coffee.

As soon as the data arrives, the printer acknowledges receipt with another low voltage signal (*Acknowledge*) sent on yet another wire. Then the whole process starts again. Anytime it needs to, the printer can send a *Busy* signal which tells the computer to hold everything until given the all clear. There is also a fault signal which stops everything if unhealthy conditions exist, such as lack of paper or a stuck ribbon.

As you can send all the bits at once rather than one after the other, parallel communications are fast and accurate, because it's easy to identify which bit is which just by knowing what wire it came in on, and when. Thus, because you're not carrying the overheads of extra bits for error checking, as with serial (below), it's possible to transfer data very efficiently, but only for short distances, as noise and signal deterioration increase rapidly with distance.

This is fortunate because trying to arrange long cables of the thicknesses needed for parallel communications around corners is very frustrating — and more so if a separate ground wire is twisted with each signal wire to reduce interference. If you couple this with separate switching arrangements for each wire, you can see that parallel transmission has the potential for being impractical and horrendously expensive.

Serial

Serial transmission involves sending data bits one after the other, down one cable. This is not as standard a method as parallel, and is slower, but it is more flexible in terms of distance.

It's quite possible to communicate with just three wires — one to transmit information, one to receive it and another to act as a ground return path but, in practice, you need others for the same reasons as you need them for parallel; the computers have to talk to each other and co-ordinate their activities. Having said that, you very rarely need more than five, and eight at the most.

Of the various standards that were laid down to straighten things out, the best known one relating to serial is *Recommended Standard 232 revision C* — you've probably already seen the term RS232C used somewhere (see Chapter 8, if not).

In Europe, another standard exists (V24) which is actually based on RS232C, so to all intents and purposes they can be regarded as being the same.

The problem is that they were hashed out when equipment was relatively primitive, and were meant to allow you to use the computer with the telephone lines. In later years serial transmission has often been used for something it was never designed to do, such as drive a printer, or a terminal. Earlier computer manufacturers also adapted unused pins for their own purposes, allowing many incompatibilities to creep in.

Although the original serial plugs catered for 25 connections (see left, below), the 9-pin version (on the right) has more or less taken over, as some of the connections in the larger plug are only backups in case the main ones don't work, and many aren't used anyway.

UART

Because data inside a computer is moved around in parallel, it must be converted if it needs to be sent to the outside world down one wire.

The *Universal Asynchronous Receiver/Transmitter* (UART) is the gadget that does this.

Originally, the 8250 design in the IBM PC was good enough, as the computer itself was a slow beast anyway. The 8250 was replaced by the 16450 when the AT was made; it did the same job, but slightly faster. The advent of Windows and high-powered machines (not necessarily together) has meant that another solution is needed because both have a single-character buffer which must be cleared before the next arrives. If the PC takes too long to do this, (250 milliseconds at 38,400 bits per second is long enough!), that character could be lost.

It's not just a matter of speed, but responsiveness. When multitasking (as with Windows), you could get problems as low as 2400 bps if the computer is slow enough at responding to interrupts, or going in and out of protected mode.

The 16550A is a pin-compatible replacement for the 16450 which contains twin 16-byte buffers (for transmit and receive) that can hold 16 characters each until the Central Processor is ready to process them (the first attempt at the 16550 had a bug in it, hence the improved A version). Although this means that the Central Processor doesn't have to service the UART so often, it's not the whole story with regard to performance. For more on this, see *Performance* in *Modems*, in Chapter 5. The buffers need to be activated by software.

Multiplexing

When connecting computers (or buildings) together, your first instinct would probably be to join each one with a dedicated channel, but this is an expensive and inefficient way of doing things as the full capacity of it would never be taxed by a single user, and at least 45 cables would be needed to link only 10 machines together.

This could be expensive, so it's far more economical to combine many channels together and have them share a single line — costs are saved by laying only one cable and the gaps caused by one person leaving the line idle could be utilised by others as well.

Multiplexing is simply the process of sending multiple signals down one channel, or even several channels down one cable, so a multiplexer is a concentrating device. This way, a large group of speech connections, say a 100, can make do with something like 40 both-way circuits. Mind you, sending signals this way is a bit like driving along the motorway — disastrous if you're not at the same speed and going the same way as the other traffic!

Multiplexing is a widely used approach to integrating voice and data traffic, and *bandwidth management* allocates resources to voice and data as required; *on demand*, if needed, to suit traffic that may come in bursts.

There are several ways of multiplexing, and the methods vary according to whether the signals are analogue or digital.

Frequency Division Multiplexing

Because electrical circuits (like radio) can be tuned to accept some frequencies and reject others, you can send several signals along one medium without them interfering with each other.

As there are several channels available, this is sometimes referred to as a *broadband* system (the bottom channel is often called the *baseband*). If nothing is being transmitted, capacity is wasted.

When you're sending messages both ways at the same time, whatever bandwidth you have available needs to be split in half, so *guard bands* are inserted between two information carrying frequencies to separate them and reduce the chances of overlap. They will carry no information, so will be easily identifiable. As guard bands take up even more space, the practical bandwidth for whatever channel you use is even more restricted.

FDM is used for limited numbers of constantly used low bandwidth channels where cost is a factor (such as long-distance connections on the telephone system).

Time Division Multiplexing

For multiplexing digital transmissions, little bits of data are sent in succession and the time on the link is sliced in strict rotation so that the data is interleaved in frames that occupy a strict portion of time, in other words, each chunk of data is given a *time slot*.

A good analogy is a contraflow, where vehicles gather at the start, are forced into a single line of traffic, and spread out again at the end.

Although it sounds fraught with difficulty, TDM happens so quickly that it looks as if a constant stream of activity is occurring on each circuit. As there is no need for guard bands, the entire channel bandwidth is used to transmit each bit. When nothing is sent, zeros are transmitted to maintain synchronisation of the whole system.

Although TDM was designed for digital systems, it can be used for analogue signals with the help of *Pulse Code Modulation*, a system which converts the smooth analogue signals to digital by sampling them several thousand times a second (8000, actually).

Demand Multiplexing

With both systems (FDM and TDM), there will be empty capacity as some users become idle. *Demand Multiplexing* will allocate empty slots as required to terminals that actually have something to send, but this is most often used on TDM.

Protocols

Having looked briefly at the signals and their carriers, we now need to establish some procedures so they can all do their work properly. If you were telephoning somebody you didn't know very well, you might start by checking that you've got the right number, then the right person, and ask them a few questions to check their reaction to what you're going to ask them. You would also know that you're not supposed to talk to them until they've finished talking to you.

In computer terms, you would be establishing a *protocol*, or specific rules to follow when communicating (red tape, if you like). Each protocol consists of a *character set* (or alphabet, as used in a language) and specifies the order and priorities of the way information is exchanged using it; protocols may also have ways of detecting and correcting errors.

Only devices using the same protocol can communicate directly with each other, and some of those available are fully explained in Chapter 20. Protocol of some sort is needed for all types of communication, serial or parallel.

The use of protocols comes under all levels of the OSI model, and the processes range from the simplicity of sending an extra bit tacked on the end of each character, to something much more complex used for satellite communications, which will incorporate methods of dealing with delays (Chapter 14).

NOTES

4

Data Transmission Schemes

There are several ways of allowing movement around a communications circuit, but at least two ways of defining each! This is because one Standards Authority has said one thing and others something entirely different.

As with the OSI model, the movement of information between computers is similar in many ways to sending trains round a railway system, which may make it easier for you to imagine. The computers (and any equipment that may be attached to them) are the stations, and the links between them are the tracks. The information itself behaves like the carriages, but we'll leave the engines and guards' vans alone for a moment.

The ITU-T (remember them?) defines:

- **Simplex** as where two way transmission is possible, but only in one direction at a time (for you railway buffs, that's "one engine in steam", with only one line available and a single engine moving the carriages either way — one engine can't go both ways at once, so control is effectively handed over to the other direction at the end of each transmission). This is like using the radio where you press a switch to talk and say "over" when finished.

- **Half Duplex** as where simultaneous two-way transmission is possible (i.e. two lines for Duplex as described below are available), but the equipment only allows it in one direction at a time (like telex, which has the wires joined up, but can't use them), and

- **Duplex** as allowing full simultaneous two-way transmission with two channels, like a radio telephone, so you can send and receive at the same time all the time.

Everyone else in the computer industry, on the other hand (in line with North America), defines *Simplex* as allowing transmission in one direction only (which seems a bit pointless as communications should be two way to be effective), and *Half Duplex* (HDX) as where two-way transmission is possible but not at the same time, because only one path is available, like ITU-T Simplex (in fact, another name for it is *Two-Frequency Simplex*).

Full Duplex (FDX), though, is the same as ITU-T Duplex. Although, on the face of it, two links are being used for transmission, there may actually be four channels, two for the data and two for ground return. These could be either separate or multiplexed, and the reason for having this many is because the whole bandwidth was designed to be used in one direction only; as there were two wires in the first place, another two were used for the opposite direction. *Four-wire circuits*, as they are known, will tend to be restricted to lines not generally available to the public, otherwise known as *leased lines*.

Where only one channel is being used for two way transmission, a special signal is required to hand over control to the other end so that transmission can go the other way. Again, just like a radio.

Synchronisation

For computers to start exchanging information, they both have to know exactly when to expect the first bit to arrive and when the last one has been sent.

The problem with teleprinters was synchronising several motors at each end of the line, all of which had varying amounts of slack in their linkages caused by wear and design problems (this is one of the technological reasons for sticking with the Baudot Code for so long, because the chances of error with only five bits per character were so much reduced).

Asynchronous Communications

As information couldn't be sent at a constant pace, it was sent at random intervals, with each side being able to stop the other if it couldn't keep up. The arrival of each character was acknowledged by the receiver sending a *receipt message* to the sender, so a new character could go any time the *stop bits* of the preceding one had been received.

To identify each character, extra bits are added to the basic 8; *start bits* at the front and *stop bits* at the back (like attaching an engine and a guard's van to the railway carriages).

The stop bit is actually a positive low voltage (or *mark*) on the line which indicates an idle condition, and remains in force until the next character is ready to be sent, so as soon as the start bit is received (indicated by a high voltage condition lasting for one time unit), the receiver knows it has to get its act together and synchronise with the sender to receive the incoming character, which it does by starting its own clock.

The use of a stop bit is not so much to signify the end of a character (although this is useful), but to provide as much contrast as possible between it and the start bit, so the start bit is actually recognised as one.

Although the transmission speeds of sender and receiver would be the same when a character is being sent (for obvious reasons), they couldn't be said to be in continuous synchronisation, hence the term *asynchronous communications*, which actually means "not synchronised". As they are actually locked in step when a character is being sent, a better description could possibly be "self-synchronised". Even better, "start-stop" communications, which it sometimes is.

You've probably already guessed that the closer tolerances allowed by modern technology mean that the number of bits per character can be increased from 5 to 8, which allows computers to transmit ASCII codes comfortably.

Asynchronous communication is used over the telephone system because the calls may be routed here, there and everywhere, and proper synchronisation of everything would be impossible.

The main problem with adding stop and start bits is that fewer characters are sent per total number of bits. To send a complete message therefore takes more time than the speeds of transmission would imply.

This isn't so important when you're at your terminal scratching your head and thinking what to say, but it could make you impatient when you just want to get on with sending large volumes of previously prepared data and the telephone company is sitting there clocking up the units.

Synchronous Communications

Synchronous communications, on the other hand, are specially geared to fast and high rates of data transfer, because they are strictly coordinated, with the computers being locked in step from the start of the transmission stream. Data is sent in blocks with checking and acknowledgement.

No start or stop bits are required, although others are added for counting purposes, so it's still important to be able to distinguish between bits, characters and complete messages. This is done by simply counting the expected number of bits and ticking them off as they come in.

It's difficult to distinguish between individual bits unless the clock signal is available at both ends of the system, so it's sent with the data.

Synchronous protocols were originally designed by IBM for its mainframes, the idea being (as with any development) to cheaply and quickly pack in more data per channel. Other manufacturers got on the bandwagon and those standards have become commonplace.

One of the first protocols was called BISYNC (short for *Binary Synchronous Transmission*). With BISYNC, data may be sent in ASCII, or any of two other character sets, and is sent in *frames*, each of which is marked by two special synchronisation characters. After these follow *header characters* (which contain identification codes) and the actual text followed by a *checksum* for the detection of errors.

A half-duplex circuit is sufficient for this as messages are only sent one way at a time, but it will work on full duplex, even though it's inefficient in terms of cost relative to work done.

While BISYNC is character orientated, HDLC (*High-level Data Link Control*) is based on bits, and is actually defined in the OSI model (it's used by X.25 at the Datalink Layer). In theory, the text of a message can be any length, but is usually restricted to multiples of 8 bits. The exact size will depend on the receiver.

BISYNC uses a special bit to indicate the number of characters in a message, whereas HDLC uses a totally unique code to indicate the beginning and end of it. This code cannot be mistaken for anything else and is called *The Flag*. It consists of a 0 followed by 6 1-bits and another 0. Whenever the link is idle the flag is sent continually.

Although because it handles multiples of 8 bits it effectively handles a byte at a time, HDLC is regarded as *bit based* because each one is scrutinised for anything that could be mistaken for The Flag. IBM uses something similar to HDLC, but with a few differences, which is called *Synchronous Data Link Control* (or SDLC).

More modern systems use a system called *isochronous*, where the timing is tied to a timescale and controlled by the network rather than the machines themselves.

The advantages of synchronous transmission over asynchronous are speed (anywhere between 20-30% quicker) and better detection of errors by the use of more effective methods (see *parity*, later). One disadvantage is that some methods encode data as non-ASCII (e.g. EBCDIC), which is one reason why special translation facilities are needed for a PC to link properly with a mainframe.

Signal Distortion

We've already seen that signals can be affected by *attenuation* and *crosstalk*, but there are other nasties about.

Noise

You've probably heard it already – the crackling on the telephone line that sounds like somebody's frying eggs on it. Where faster transmission speeds are stretching the capabilities of the line, data becomes less robust and can easily be affected by even small amounts of *noise*. "Noise" in electrical terms means unwanted and unpredictable impulses, breaks in transmission or extra signals, which can be thought of as extra electricity on the line, so you can see that a 0 could be made to look like a 1 if the noise level is high enough, and *vice versa*.

Noise is measured in *decibels* relative to the signal associated with it, and the comparison of one to the other is known as the *Signal to Noise Ratio* (the decibel is named after Alexander Graham Bell). The scale of measurement is logarithmic, so that a signal to noise ratio twice as good as another is actually only increased by 3 decibels.

Noise is always present in electrical circuits and there are many types. The Man-made stuff is easily detected and is more spontaneous; crossed lines, car ignition interference, fridges turning themselves on and off, etc. Other examples include static and the sort of clicks and pops heard when tuning between radio stations. As such, it is only predictable within certain statistical limits.

Distortion

You can often hear a background hiss (or "rushing" noise) in between records on a radio, even when it's correctly tuned; this is noise being generated within the circuitry itself by all the collisions between the molecules and atoms as the signal moves.

The most common is a low background noise called *white noise* (or *thermal noise*) and it occurs whenever there is resistance to electrical movement (it's called white noise because it covers a wide range of frequencies at a constant level, rather like white light).

Unfortunately, amplifying the signal so you can hear it better also succeeds in amplifying the noise, so the object of the exercise is defeated somewhat.

If everything were perfect, the signal would travel at 186,000 miles per second (the speed of light, which is also an electromagnetic force) but, practically, this speed reduces to about 14,000 miles per second on ordinary twisted pair cable or 100,000 miles per second where microwaves are used. This is because of resistance.

These slower speeds mean that there is a calculable delay between sending and receipt, which can be allowed for, but the length of the delay also varies with the frequency of the signal, being greater with lower frequencies.

This is OK when you're only sending one signal, but if you're sending two at different frequencies, with the content of each being dependent on the other, there could be some corruption if they're out of phase with each other at the receiving end.

These constant effects can be simply calculated in accordance with known formulae and allowed for as far as possible in the design stages. Instead of merely allowing for certain effects, though, it's possible to do something about some of them. For example, one way of dealing with delays between two signals (called *phase shift*, by the way) is to introduce some sort of *delay equalisation* that helps compensate. There's more about error correction in Chapter 6.

5

Telephone Lines

Unless the computers that need to talk are sitting next to each other, there needs to be some way of connecting them over long distances which, for practical purposes, means the telephone system (commonly called the PSTN in the computer industry, the letters standing for *Public Switched Telephone Network*).

Depending on your requirements, that is, the amount of information you want to send (and how well you want it received at either end), together with the equipment you propose to use, there are two main categories of available lines.

Standard Telephone Connection

Otherwise known as a *dial-up line*, this has a theoretical capacity of 20,640 bps (bits per second) if analogue, although this is generally unavailable without special procedures and equipment. A digital line can give around 24,000, but most connections to digital exchanges are analogue (except ISDN – see the end of this chapter).

Dedicated Line

Also known as a *leased line*, this is a permanent sole-use connection usually rented out to commercial organisations (because they are the only ones who can afford them) with a better signal-to-noise ratio. A flat monthly fee is paid, based on speed and distance, and should be considered if you expect to connect to the same place more than 4-6 hours a day. One example is the type of lines allocated to the emergency services, or those connecting High Street cash machines to a central bank.

Typical services available over leased lines include:

- **Kilostream**, which is a digital leased line that provides high speed links between terminals and computers up to 48-64,000 bps, and

- **Megastream**, which is as above, but up to 140 mbps for data or PABX links, so you can include the telephone exchanges in each building. A 2 Mb link can carry up to 30 voice channels, which can be multiplexed to combine voice and data as required.

Both standard or leased lines, however, are unable to carry computer signals as they stand, so you need translation facilities at each end to make them talk properly.

For translation, you need two pieces of equipment; a *modulator* (which converts the computer's digital signals into tones of varying pitch) at the sending station and a *demodulator* (which swaps them round again) at the receiver. As most data transmission is two way, the same equipment is needed at each end.

Modems

Modem is short for *Mo*dulator/*Dem*odulator. It's a device that combines the two functions described above; that is, it converts the on/off signals that a computer uses into audio tones so they can be sent down a telephone line and *vice versa*. This conversion is known as *changing the modulation*, hence the name. A digital line would have a *Digital Service Unit*, or *Digital Modem* (if you're wondering why, it's because you still need protocol conversion, even though the signals are similar).

A modem plugs directly into a normal telephone socket, and connects to your PC's serial port (or parallel port for the more powerful types), so it sits between your computer and the telephone socket. Some are internal, so you can keep the desk tidy, but you can't watch the indicator lights to see what's going on.

As they're connected to the telephone system, modems must also be approved by the *British Approvals Board for Telecommunications* (look for the green label). This "approval", however, is only to check that it doesn't muck up the system as far as BABT is concerned – it's not a consumer test of facilities and performance.

It is illegal to connect anything to the telephone system that hasn't gone through the official approval procedures (and passed!). Mind you, it isn't illegal to buy or sell it – only to connect it.

Amplitude Shift Keying

The simplest way of representing binary information with tones is to have one volume equal to 1 and another equal to 0 but, as with AM radio, this is susceptible to noise and will only allow a rate of about 1200 signals per second over the cable.

Frequency Shift Keying

FSK is similar to ASK, except that the *frequency* of the signal is changed rather than the *amplitude*, giving the same comparison as FM radio against AM. As there is less noise, the system is more robust and you can get up to 2400 signals per second.

Phase Shift Keying

PSK changes the *position* of a signal relative to another, so a change in phase of 180° will signify a 1; no change represents a 0. This produces twice the signalling rate of FSK. *Differential PSK* allows 2 or more bits to be encoded per signal (see also *QAM*, below).

Acoustic Couplers

Very early types of modem were acoustic couplers which had rubber cups into which you placed your telephone handset.

They are modems to which are attached a loudspeaker and a microphone that are held near the handset's mouthpiece and earpiece respectively. This can be cheap and convenient, but the variety of strange shaped handsets around has effectively ruled out the use of acoustic couplers on anything but the old-fashioned type. Having said that, modern ones are still available because of the different types of phone sockets (or lack of them) around the world!

Their main disadvantage lies in their accoustic and not electrical connection – it's always possible for odd noises to get in around the seals and ruin the signal.

Operating Speeds

A real modem's direct connection eliminates outside noise, but the characteristics of the telephone line will limit your speeds (it only has 2700 Hz bandwidth available), which will get less as the quality of the lines deteriorates; this will actually change from moment to moment, what with routing through sub-standard lines, etc.

The slowest practical speed is 300 bits per second; the fastest with analogue transmissions is 2400, without special treatment. If you go any faster, you will need more bandwidth, which is simply not available, so techniques have been developed that will allow you send more signals, if you can't actually make the signals go faster, such as *Differential PSK*, mentioned previously. With a digital exchange, however, you get a better *signal to noise ratio*, together with a much increased bandwidth (up to 3429 Hz), so faster speeds are possible, but not necessarily between your computer and the exchange; the improvements are averaged over the whole connection.

We've mentioned *bits per second* quite a bit already. This speaks for itself, but the term *baud* (named after Baudot) is sometimes loosely used in place of it – the "baud" rate is actually the frequency of the modem tone, and therefore the number of *signal changes a second* (as opposed to the *amount of data transmitted*, represented by bits per second). In the case of early modems, the terms coincide, because one bit will be represented by one change in the signal.

Where more than one bit is sent for each change of signal (as you would get when more information is squeezed on to the tone), the two terms part company. For all practical purposes, though, any modem below 2400 baud is customarily regarded as operating at a corresponding rate of bits per second.

A "9600 baud modem", by the way, is actually a 2400 baud one using *Quadrature Amplitude Modulation*, which transmits 4 bits per baud, so it should actually be called a "9600 bps modem". QAM modifies the carrier wave to be in one of four states, each $90°$ removed from each other. 14,400 modems are still 2400 baud, but use *Trellis Coded Modulation* on top, giving six bits per baud. You can get twelve bits per baud with *Multidimensional TCM*, giving you 28,800 bps, but the lines have to be spot-on for this; 24,000 would be more typical.

Unfortunately, software doesn't recognise such terms, and you will always get an average speed of around 1000 characters per second unless you use data compression as well, to boost your *effective* speed.

For example, if you have a 14,400 bps modem running V.42*bis* (see below), you will probably be able to connect at 38,400 (but your software should not autolock to modem speeds).

Data compression is the process of reducing the size of what is sent without damaging it, so more can be moved in a given time (cheaper phone bills!). One method is *Run Length Encoding*, which takes the first one of a sequence of the same characters and attaches a note to it, saying how many more there are. Another way is vary the number of bits representing a character, according to its frequency of use.

Your final transmission rate will therefore depend upon the ability of the data to be compressed, as well as the capabilities of the computers at each end (more in *Performance*, overleaf).

Modem speeds are usually written thus: 2400/2400 or 1200/75. The slash is used because modems transmit as well as receive; the first number denotes the receiving speed and the second that used for transmitting. In Europe, the standards relating to computer communications by telephone come under the V series, where V is short for the French *Vitesse*, meaning speed. On the other hand, it could mean *Study Group 5* (of CCITT). It's mostly called *Veedot*, though, by those in the know.

Here are some of the modem standards you may come across:

V.19/20	Relates to parallel modems.
V.21	300/300 Old FSK Full Duplex asynchronous. Really out of date.
V.22	1200/1200 PSK Half Duplex asynchronous. Very much out of date.
V.22 bis	2400/2400 Full Duplex asynchronous. Sort of out of date, but still useable in some cases.
V.23	1200/75 FSK Full Duplex asynchronous. Still used, but out of date.
V.24	Definitions for circuits between Transmission equipment (e.g. RS232).
V.25	Control language that lost out to Hayes (see below), but is being regenerated.
V.32	9600/9600 Full Duplex asynchronous.

V.32 bis	14400/14400.
V.32 ter	Unofficial extension to V32 to 19200 bps.
V.34	28800/28800 (*V.Fast* was the unofficial version of this). Actually up to 115kbps with V42bis (i.e. compression), giving 1 Mb every 2 minutes or so.
V.42	Error correction, using LAP-M, but superseded by MNP4 (see Chapter 6).
V.42 bis	Error correction, with compression, so superceding MNP5. Can autodetect compressed files and turn off compression automatically for them. Compresses at 4-1.

V.FC was an interim standard put forward by Rockwell and Hayes whilst waiting for V.34 to be sorted out.

Performance

Unfortunately, a 14.400 bps modem using V.42*bis* (i.e. compression) will need data sent to it at three to four times that rate in order to keep throughput up; in other words, you need to run the serial port at 38,400 or 57,600 bps. It's worse with V.34, at 28,800 bps; with compression, you will need to shift data at greater than 115,000 bps!

What performance you finally get will depend on many factors, including your BIOS, other hardware and the software you use to communicate. The "other hardware" will most likely be Network Interface Cards (see Chapter 16), which can hog interrupts and therefore interfere with serial communications, or inefficient hard disk controllers, which will do the same thing. The data you wish to send, and its compressibility, has a bearing, as well.

Windows

Windows doesn't help, either. Aside from the fact that you may not have a 16550 UART in your machine, and you can only load one comms driver anyway, a computer that's 286- based will typically take about 1 ms to change from protected to real mode, as interrupts are serviced to process data transmissions (this is called *interrupt latency*). Thus, the fastest transmission rate possible is 4800 or 9600 bps, depending on the amount of time taken for switching.

Although 386- and 486-based machines switch faster (1000 times per second at 9600 bps, and over 11,000 for 115,200 bps), Windows' virtualisation of the COM port means that you could still get problems when running faster than 19,200 bps.

Windows is also set to interrupt the CPU when the 16550's receive buffer reaches 14 bytes, which is only one character better than the old 16450 could handle anyway, so you're not that much better off. Lastly, Windows doesn't make use of the transmit buffer. It's not all bad news, though – third party comms drivers are available, and many Windows comms programs can handle this by themselves.

So, with a 16450/8250 on a 486DX2-66, standard Windows communications can only support up to 38.4 Kbps during a file transfer, possibly smaller, depending on disk access times, etc. It's not that much better with a 16550, so it's always possible to get data overruns and lose characters, especially if you're communicating in the background and using a DOS-based application that accesses the hard disk frequently (more protected mode switching). Even if you don't lose characters, the retransmissions needed to keep them all intact will slow things down.

The above has led to the development of modems that use the parallel port. As they receive 8 bits at a time, instead of one, data can be delivered in bursts (up to 64 characters), thus making better use of interrupts available. Fewer interrupts mean that the CPU can get on with other things; parallel modems can reduce the interrupt rate to just 360 per second (compare this with 5,500 even with a 16550). This can be reduced even further by increasing the packet size.

There are also enhanced serial ports, such as the *Hayes ESP-II*, that have 1K buffers, but they need the correct software to run properly. The interrupt count can be reduced to 11 per second with these, giving you much smoother processing.

Hayes

Once upon a time, an American company called *Hayes Microcomputer Products* made the *Smartmodem* – "smart" meaning that it was intelligent, and able to be controlled by commands from the computer rather than having its buttons pushed on the front. A Hayes modem has a microprocessor inside, which is fed instructions from the software you use on your PC.

Hayes developed their own programming language which has become a standard, at least for the basic commands (listed below); their software commands are known as the *Hayes Command Set*.

Through these, a modem can be programmed to do all sorts of things in quick succession, including dialling a number, changing speed, hanging up – in fact anything others usually do with switches.

All you do is prefix the commands with the letters AT. These letters were chosen because their bit pattern makes it easier for the modem to detect what sort of data is coming from the computer, and at what speed (in other words, the modem sets its own speed according to how the letters AT are sent). For convenience, you could think of them as being short for "ATtention".

Each time it sees **AT**, the modem sends back a result code to tell the software what went on. You can have up to 40 more characters after AT, but this may vary between manufacturers.

As an example, to dial someone, just key in (from your keyboard when your communications software's in *terminal mode*):

    ATD

followed by the number – the full phrase:

    ATDP01818368876

(you can put spaces in for readability) tells it to take the phone off the hook (AT), wait for the dial tone and dial (D) with pulses (P) the number that follows. If the line is engaged, the response

    BUSY

would appear on the computer screen, but you can change the phraseology if you want to.

You may get

    NO CARRIER

if it can't connect, or the word

    CONNECT

followed by the speed, when it does.

Pulse and Tone Dialling

Pulse Dialling is that used with old rotary telephones — as the dial spins round, it generates a small pulse of electricity which is recognised at the exchange; each digit is represented by the same number of pulses. Now, *Dual-Tone Multifrequency Dialling* (DTMF, or just MF) is used, where each digit is represented by an audio tone.

A Hayes modem also has a small amount of memory, so that frequently used numbers can be stored and accessed with a code consisting of considerably fewer keystrokes than normal. You can pre-program it to change speeds and other parameters as may be required, although this will be handled by your software.

Default instructions, that is, those you use all the time, are contained in the *S registers*, the number of which depends on the make. For example, *S0* stores the number of rings the modem will wait until it answers the telephone. *S6* will set the wait time for a dial tone.

The modem itself can be in two operational states — *command* or *on-line* (e.g. *data mode*). While it's in the command state you can set it up and give it all the instructions you want to; no transmission is taking place. The on-line state is when it's doing its real work. Once you're on-line, you can issue instructions as if you were in Command mode by issuing an *Escape code* consisting of plus signs that enables you to change any parameters you want on the run; the modem temporarily stops sending while you do so. Otherwise, the modem will assume that everything issued from the computer is data.

Types of AT Command

Standard AT commands are those you will find in any Hayes-compatible modem; there are about 20. They consists of AT plus a letter and an option relating to that letter (0 is assumed if nothing is given).

Extended AT commands are often thought up by different manufacturers according to what they think is useful. They generally come with a symbol, such as & or %, between AT and the command letter.

A	Autoanswer.
B	Bell or CCITT mode.
C	Enables carrier transmission.
D	Dial a number (add P or T as appropriate).
E	Concerns echo.

Q	Quiet mode, or whether it sends reports.
V	Verbose responses if Q is enabled.
Z	Software reset.

Examples

ATD	Dial number; P = Pulse T = Tone
,	Pause
ATA	Answer call.

Initialisation

Z	Reset to stored defaults.
&F	Restore factory defaults.
Sr = n	Set register Sr (*r* and *n* are numbers).

Information

E	Echo; 0 = Do not echo back AT commands to software 1 = Echo back
Q	Response to commands; 0 = Send OK (or other) 1 = Quiet; no responses given
M	Speaker; 0 = Speaker off 1 = Speaker on till connect 2 = Speaker always on

All the above commands can be combined in any order. For example, if you need to insert a pause in your telephone number (you might be on a telephone exchange which needs a couple of seconds to think to itself), simply use a comma, as with:

```
9,
```

if you need to dial 9 to get an outside line before sending the proper number. An example of a full dialling command could be:

```
ATDT9,131,,37747777789
```

The first letters, AT, get the modem's attention, D means Dial, T means *Tone* (you would use P for *Pulse*), the 9 gets you an outside line and the comma inserts a pause. 131 is the Mercury access code, which also requires a pause or two in front of it before sending your PIN number. After that, just add the number you wish to dial. You can change the length of the pause through one of the registers.

Modem Initialisation String

Sometimes a special set of commands is sent to the modem to wake it up properly when the software loads. They concern whether the speaker should be on and various other housekeeping settings (your own favourite commands, in other words). It could look something like this:

```
ATZ S=1 &F&C&D G=0
```

Don't try that one, by the way; I made it up.

Ideally, a modem initialisation string should be no more than ATZ, with the remainder of the instructions obtained from the default settings kept in the modem's memory, but you get better security if you issue a string every time, which helps if you run a Bulletin Board (see Chapter 11).

Specialised modems

Of special interest to Bulletin Boards are *scanning modems*, where a number of attached lines are read in rotation several times a second to find the first one used.

Where software cannot handle split speeds, a *buffered modem* speaks to the computer at one speed (1200/1200) and the outside world at something else (1200/75). This is sometimes known as a *constant speed interface* modem which, in addition, will use the buffer in the same way a printer does; a fast computer can send data immediately while the modem sends at its own pace.

Fax modems are common (as muck). For more about these, see Chapter 12.

MFTAM stands for *Modem, Fax, Telephone Answering Machine* all in one. They are sometimes referred to as *Voice Modems*, because many can handle voice and data transmissions at the same time, although the latter's transfer rate will drop slightly if you do.

Cable modems are used with cable TV networks to bring data services direct to your home, several hundred times faster than ordinary telephone lines, or ISDN, so you can use video clips, too.

Being In Control

On the front of the average modem, you should see lights indicating the operation of the following functions. The more automated the equipment is, the less there will be:

Power	Whether power is getting to the modem.
HS	*High Speed*; i.e. operating at maximum speed.
AA	*AutoAnswer* (where your modem answers the phone for you).
SD or Txd	*Send Data* or *Transmit Data*; data is being transmitted when this is on.
RD or Rxd	*Receive Data*; data is being received when this is on.
OH	*Off Hook*; your modem is using the phone line.
TR or DTR	*Terminal Ready* or *Data Terminal Ready*; this is normally controlled by the computer or terminal and indicates that the computer is talking to the modem. It may be marked as "Ready".
CD or DCD	Indicates that the modem has detected the remote modem's carrier signal and is happy with the quality.
RI	*Ring indicator*. Flashes in time with the ringing current on the line, usually used with auto-answer.
DC	*Data Compression*.
EC	*Error Correction*.

Non-autodial, non-Hayes compatible modems will have a switch that you operate when you hear the tones at the other end so that it can capture the line. It will be marked *Data* or *On-line*, or may even be just the power switch (that is, switching on captures the line automatically). Other controls may include Baud rate settings and possibly a reset button.

The power light should always be on, but watch for the *low power* light if your modem is battery powered. When you tell the software to connect, the DTR light will come on as the computer takes control of the line, between it and the modem.

Then the number is dialled. The incoming ringing current is recognised by the answering modem, which goes off-hook and issues a series of tones (defined by V.25) which are meant to disable echo suppression and cancellation on the line, so the modem can use its own. The originating modem sends a signal that tells the other side what speed it is running at, so it can cycle through the speeds available until connection is made, or it gets bored waiting.

The modem will inform the computer that a link has been established, and the DCD light will come on. This signal is continually monitored by the computer to check the connection has not broken.

You will see the TXD and RXD lights flash in sympathy with the data as it is transmitted and received.

Originate/Answer

When transferring information, modems use two frequencies — a high one for zeros and a low one for the 1-bits; if the two modems involved in a communications session used the same frequencies for these, you can see there would be some confusion over who sent what. To sort this out, two other sets of frequencies are used by the receiving modem, but it must be decided at the start which role the particular modems will take.

Some modems have an *Originate/Answer* switch, which is set according to what your activity is — those that don't have one set themselves automatically. The modem starting everything off is known as the *originator*. All services (such as CIX or Compuserve) are answerers.

Note that the speed sensing circuitry in some V.22*bis* modems doesn't like the phase reversals in the answer tones of a V.32*bis* one; in other words, they might have trouble connecting; this includes V.22*bis* ones masquerading as V.32*bis*. This is referred to in *Troubleshooting*, Chapter 24.

All you need is . . .

The following items will connect your PC to the telephone system:

- **The PC**, with a serial port based on RS232 (Chapter 8), or a parallel port if your modem is more powerful.

- **A modem**, which for simplicity should be Hayes compatible (that is, follows the standards laid down by Hayes). The modem needs to be connected to the PC with a cable, but you can get internal ones that go inside.

   What you buy really depends on what you want to do. If you mainly transfer files, a fast modem will pay for itself quickly, in terms of lower telephone costs and boredom.

   If most of your time is spent on-line, though, just wondering what to say next in an on-line conference, you won't really appreciate the benefits, and a 2400 modem will probably do (with compression, it will connect at a higher effective speed anyway).

   There are no official figures to tell you how good each modem is (and brochures tell lies anyway), so the best advice is to carry out your own field trials. Note that while it's true that you only get what you pay for, it's equally true that price is not necessarily a reflection of quality or features.

   Several high-end products are outperformed by less expensive competitors; for full compatibility and sheer convenience, just buy a Hayes (it will work straight out of the box) but, then again, so do others that are cheaper; still others will offer better performance. It just depends how busy you are!

   Considering that manuals are usually incomprehensible and get lost anyway, look for considerate modem manuafacturers that print useful stuff like DIP switch settings and commands on the bottom of their products.

- Since a computer only does what it's told, you also need **communications software** to send and receive data and save it to disk when necessary. More about software in Chapter 9.

- A **telephone line!**

ISDN

ISDN, or the *Integrated Services Digital Network*, is an international program for the digitisation of telephone systems in Western Europe, Japan and North America. It accepts digital data directly, and has the potential to allow voice, data, fax and video signals to be transmitted over the ordinary telephone system at the same time — you can send 150,000 or so digital words (in the form of bits) in the same time it takes to send 6 analogue ones (as a voice conversation). Up to 30 channels of varying types of information can go out on an ISDN cable simultaneously.

There are two services available, *Basic* or *Primary*, and the difference lies in the number of B channels (e.g. digital comms lines) available; 2 for Basic and 30 for Primary. There is also a D channel with each that is used to set up the call, which also has a bandwidth of 64 Kbps, but 16 is made available for call connection services, and the remainder is reserved for management functions. You would normally expect to use Basic for LAN communications; the Primary service is usually for the service providers themselves.

Both B channels can be merged for double throughput one way (called *reverse multiplexing*). This *aggregation* is quite useful when your leased line goes down; if you have them available, you can combine 10 ISDN channels to take its place (actually, ISDN was originally marketed as a backup to leased lines). A *backup unit* will automatically do the switching for you.

ISDN is already used at digital exchanges, but the connection to your telephone socket is, more often than not, analogue. Once the complete connection is made, however, the potential (for business at least) is good. Once an ISDN exchange is fitted, all the computers in the building can connect to the outside world (and to each other) without modems, although you still need a connection point, in the shape of a TA (*Terminal Adapter*). People can work from home and use the company network facilities directly, with very little loss in performance, although I wouldn't like to try and run Windows over any telephone line!

Transmission is virtually error free, you don't need compression (yet), connection is almost instantaneous (.2 seconds or so) and you get Full Duplex operation.

NOTES

6

Error Detection

Fast transmission speeds aren't everything – your information is no good if it gets there quicker but is unreadable because of errors (assuming you typed everything correctly in the first place!).

Early transmission methods had no error detection. They knew very well when each part of a message had got through, because of the acknowledgements, but these told them nothing about whether what had arrived was what had been sent ("Lead us not into Thames Station...").

Part of the process of detecting errors is guessing what the signal should have been in the first place (if the whole message is known to both sides, there's no point in sending it!). This is done by adding other information to the basic message, from which this can be deduced. What we have to do is supply enough extra data that is known by both sides to increase the chances of detecting any problems. Blocks of characters are statistically analysed as they are sent and the results of that analysis are tacked on to the end of the message and sent to the receiver, where the analysis is carried out again and the results compared.

Parity

In addition to start and stop bits, another can be used for error checking, which is called the *parity bit* (actually not often used these days, because it used to be the eighth bit when ASCII used seven).

With *parity checking*, the 1-bits making up a character are added up and, depending on whether the result is odd or even, another bit is added to make the total to the opposite. So, if the symbol contains an odd number of 1s, even parity would require another 1-bit to be added to make this number even (and odd parity would need the reverse, of course).

For instance, the character A (code 10000001) has two 1-bits. Odd parity would require the parity bit to be a 1 to make the total of 1s an odd one.

C (code 10000011) having three 1-bits would have the parity bit set to 0 as the total is already odd.

The parity generating circuit (which is usually a dedicated chip) in the sending unit counts the number of 1s and sets the parity bit as required. The receiving unit does the same and calculates what the parity bit should be. If the two match, then no error is assumed.

This works well enough, but unfortunately doesn't pick up everything – more than one error probably wouldn't be noticed, and the software rarely corrects things automatically.

Both sides have to know what sort of parity is being used. The usual options are *Even*, *Odd* or *None*, with *Mark* and *Space* as oddballs that you probably won't come across (Mark parity is always 1, and Space always 0). You should set the parity to NONE if you can get away with it, so that if the eighth bit is used for anything strange (such as a control bit) without anyone knowing, then it's left well alone – this applies particularly when sending program, or binary, files. The parity bit must be set this way for 8-bit ASCII transfer.

Checksums and CRCs

Checksums and *Cyclic Redundancy Codes* are based on blocks of data rather than single characters, unlike parity checking.

A checksum is simply a summation of the ASCII values of every byte within the block, divided by 256 and the remainder discarded. The number is sent with the data and recalculated at the other end. If it's the same, all should be well, but you could get the same checksum for a different set of bytes. It's about 60% reliable.

CRCs typically include two bytes at the end of a block which are otherwise redundant, hence the name. These values are calculated by dividing the entire numeric binary value of the block by a constant figure (called a *generator polynomial* – no, I don't know what it means, either, but you get the general idea). It's about 99% reliable.

CRC can be used in conjunction with parity.

Error Correction

Since a bit can be either on or off, and valid even if it is an error, it would be much more useful if a system could describe exactly where an error is and correct it, rather than just detecting its presence, as the previously mentioned systems are only capable of doing. As far as correcting errors goes, commonly used systems are *Forward Error Correction* (FEC), *Backward Error Correction*, *Automatic Repeat Request* (ARQ), *Microcom Networking Protocol* (MNP) and *V42*.

Forward Error Correction

Forward Error Checking allows reconstruction because the message contains extra information specially for the purpose. Correction is done at the *forward* end (i.e. the receiver) so the message does not have to be repeated, and the next block can be sent without waiting for acknowledgements.

FEC uses *Hamming Codes* in place of ASCII, where 11 bits represent a character instead of 7 (or 8). The extra bits are redundant and are interspersed amongst the rest so that the position of the erroneous bit can be calculated from the remaining ones. Once that's been found out, then that bit is inverted, since it can only be a 0 or a 1. However, like parity checking, this only provides protection against single-bit errors.

It's actually more efficient to send data again than to try and fix it (see *Backward Error Correction*), so FEC is more often used where data can't be retransmitted, such as on backup tapes, or with satellite transmission, as other methods involve a time delay between acknowledge and receipt.

Backward Error Correction

Errors are still detected at the receiver, but the transmitter resends the offending data, so this is actually a form of error control, since bad data is not corrected, but discarded. A file is divided into blocks or frames and CRC check sequences are added to each block.

Automatic Repeat reQuest

With ARQ, a CRC or checksum is calculated for each block and added to it when transmitted. At the receiving end, the CRC or checksum is recalculated, and compared to the original checksum value. If the two agree, then all is (theoretically) well.

If not, a NAK (Negative Acknowledgement) is sent back to request retransmission. One common ARQ protocol is Xmodem, described in Chapter 10. ARQ is often used as a synonym for.....

Microcom Networking Protocol

MNP, invented by Microcom, provides error correction between two similarly equipped modems by automatically sending erroneous data in packets until everything has been properly transmitted. Most MNP-equipped modems do this without you interfering.

MNP allows continuous data transmission — you don't need the extra bits round each character to help identify each one.

However, MNP doesn't work quite so well with high speed modems as it does with with medium speed ones, due to the time required to recover from line noise. As a result, most use *Trellis encoding*, or *Forward Error Detection* as well, where the receiving modem automatically detects and corrects errors before the data is passed on to the PC, effectively filtering out the line noise caused by faulty equipment, and separating the data from noise.

MNP 1-4	In the Public Domain. No more need be said about these, except that the first two actually reduced throughput, level 3 improved things slightly, and level 4 had automatic adjustment of frame sizes.
MNP 5	Introduced data compression (at around 2-1) to boost throughput, but it is applied regardless, and can make pre-compressed files take longer to be transmitted.
MNP 6	Designed for high speed half-duplex connections between 4800-9600 bps.
MNP 7	As level 5, with better data compression.
MNP 9	As for earlier levels, but with improvements when deciding optimum modulation levels and protocols.
MNP 10	An advanced method for adverse line conditions. It can reduce speed when conditions are bad, and *vice versa*, so is used for cellular transmission (e.g. mobile phones).

V.42

A CCITT (ITU-T) version of error correction, which means less royalties for Microcom. This supersedes MNP4. V.42*bis* provides data compression with autodetection for compressed files, so it doesn't try to do the same job twice.

7

Switching

Switching gets around the need to connect every station to each other (imagine the wires!), and allows better use of the bandwidth available by ensuring that only those stations that need to talk are actually connected at any time. Excess traffic is not therefore circulating round the system and clogging it all up.

Circuit Switching

A circuit switched communications system (e.g. the telephone) consists of a number of exchanges interconnected by *trunks* (major direct connections), each capable of switching to alternate circuits if a call can't get through on a particular route. The circuits are used for the duration of the call (that is, the connection is permanent as long as it's needed), then are disconnected into their component parts for reuse in other switched circuits. The connection to your exchange (i.e. from your telephone), on the other hand, is permanent.

Message Switching

Where data is concerned, immediate feedback (and the need for continuous interconnection) is not so important, so permanent circuits are not only unnecessary, but wasteful.

As a fast response is not required, the system only needs to deliver to a specified address, so the emphasis turns to reliable delivery, at the cost of some delays. As well as the data being sent, the total message will consist of address and identification information concerning the sending and receiving stations. This means that, whereas a circuit switching system needs to wait for a path to be set up before data can be sent, a message switching system can send at once and wait for the links to made later.

Some message switching terminals have a memory facility which is used as a temporary message store. If the trunk is busy, the message can be stored until the channel is free. This is often known as a *Store-and-Forward* system.

Storing messages provides a way of avoiding peaks during periods of high system load, so that an engaged tone doesn't matter so much — all messages will eventually get through, provided they contain all the necessary routing information.

Packet Switching

Packet switching, although superficially similar to message switching, is distinct from it in that a message is split up into packets (say 512 bits long) which don't even have to go in convoy; each segment is "wrapped" with extra information which includes its address and sequence in the original message so that it doesn't get lost, rather like Paddington Bear.

Packets are transmitted individually over the system, being given the best routing by the control nodes, according to traffic jams, and reassembled at the receiving terminal. There's no real intelligence involved here; the packets are merely routed nearer and nearer to their destination until they hit (of course, this happens so quickly that you don't notice). On the link, packets from one conversation are very likely to be interleaved with packets from others, which means that they must be relatively small to allow for maximum flexibility (if you're trying to fit parcels in a small space, it's easier to fill the space economically with several small ones than a few large ones).

Packet Switching was first proposed in the US in 1964 as a way of controlling data transmission without a dedicated channel between sender and receiver — in other words, multiple signals can be sent down one carrier and redistributed at the other end. This makes the use of one line more efficient as spare capacity can be used when it's idle. However, what usually happens is that normal permanent connections are used and the segments fit in between the gaps left in normal speech transmission, thus allowing them to hitchhike a lift at greatly reduced rates over long distances.

As has been said, the most appropriate route of the packet is determined by controlling computers or nodes. Sometimes packets may be stored in them temporarily, which is not usually noticeable as the delays are seldom more than a fraction of a second. You will not be surprised to hear that there are standards laid down for packet switched networks as well, one of which is CCITT (or ITU-T) recommendation X.25 (X means digital transmissions).

X.25

X.25 has been the most widely used protocol for packet switching since 1976, but is slowly becoming obsolete due to improvements in technology; the restrictions it was to overcome are getting fewer.

X.25 requires that data is split up into small packets labelled with origination and destination addresses, and sequencing information (so you know in which order it goes). The data itself can be of any form, from Baudot to Binary.

An X.25 network is often represented by a cloud, because of the mysterious ways a packet could be routed to its destination (all you really need to know is that a packet goes in, and comes out where you want it). In other words, a *virtual circuit* (VC) is established; stations know of a connection between them, but not the details of it. Switched VCs are set up as and when needed, and Permanent VCs are established in advance.

Most users of X.25 require equipment to conform to a standard called GOSIP, or *Government OSI Profile* (those initials again).

X.25 can be used privately, around the company or over leased lines, but it's more commonly used with the PSS.......

The Packet Switch Stream

This is a system specially designed to handle data transmission. It was established properly in 1981, but is now part of BT's GNS (Global Network Services). It's a data network which closely resembles a telephone system, but is meant for computers and other equipment that speak digitally.

It provides full duplex communications between connected terminals using standardised data packets and is based directly on CCITT protocol X.25 (and related recommendations).

Because it uses high-quality dedicated data lines which can allow one cable to take several calls (using multiplexing), it's very cheap to use. You can link into the PSS at a local "node", one of which can be found in each major city. This means that a call across the Atlantic need cost no more than a local one, but you still have to be a subscriber.

To get on to it (apart from handing over your cash), you need equipment capable of sending and receiving packets.

You can either create the packets yourself with a *packet terminal,* which is a specialised computer that gets on to the system through a dedicated Dataline, or dial up the system directly with your own computer and let them do it.

If you do dial the system, it will be to a *packet assembler/dissassembler* (PAD), which is essentially a protocol converter which takes a stream of data and sandwiches it between packet information that is discarded when the message arrives at its destination.

PADS, therefore, accept your incoming data (automatically selecting speed, parity, etc) and send it along the PSS. At the other end, they change everything round again, still doing automatic error detection.

You will need a *Network User Identity* (NUI). For the other end, you will need a *Network User Address* (NUA) to which you send your data, which will probably also require a password.

Each country's *Packet Switched Data Network* (PSDN) is identified with a DNIC, or *Data Network Identification Code.*

Both the NUI and NUA consist of 12 digits of which the first 3 refer to the country, the 4th to the service within that country (e.g. the four together make the DNIC) and the rest to the terminal itself. The DNIC must precede everything else.

Frame Relay

This connects at up to 2.048 Mb/s, so is faster than X.25 at 64 Kbps. This is because it doesn't do so much error checking, so it has less overheads to cope with. That's left to software at each end of the link, saving you from doing the same job twice.

A *Frame Assembler/Disassembler* (FAD) is needed for Frame relay; it does a similar job to a PAD on X.25.

X.400

X.25 is used for transmitting small packets of information, but there is no way of ensuring compatibility between formats at either end, which is where X.400 comes in, providing a message and address structure that helps to ensure that the data is actually understood by the receiving station, whatever it's being run by. Basically, X.400 provides an "envelope" for the individual letters sent by X.25 — what starts as a complete letter arrives as such and is sent to the right place.

RS232

We mentioned previously that the telephone side of a modem only needs two wires. The wiring to the computer, on the other hand, is much more complex, and this is what we will look into now. Don't forget that systems using the RS232 standard do not necessarily use all of the connections – a product that is "RS232 compatible" just means that where they are used, they meet the specifications laid down.

DTE and DCE

The RS232 and V24 standards refer specifically to connections between modems and computers. In doing this, they describe two types of equipment which are a mirror image of each other, as far as wiring between them goes, anyway.

The terminal (e.g. a computer or printer) is known as *Data Terminal Equipment* (DTE) and almost everything else, e.g. a modem, as *Data Circuit-terminating Equipment* (DCE).

The difference is that DCE equipment terminates a line; it collects the information and passes it on to a DTE, which actually does something with it, such as put it on the screen, save it to disk or print it. In other words, a DCE will convert a DTE's signals into something suitable for whatever it wants to transmit over, and *vice versa*.

How you wire everything up depends on whether you're connecting DTE to DCE (computer to modem) or DTE to DTE (computer to computer, terminal or printer), and whether you use a male or female connector sometimes rests on the same premise (this also depends on the manufacturer of your equipment). However, if you connect a DTE to a DTE which is expecting to talk to a DCE, then there will be some confusion as transmission will try to go both ways down the same wire! Pin connections mentioned in the standards refer to DTE equipment and must be viewed from this standpoint.

Handshaking

Although in theory you could just use the MODE command on each computer to set them to the same speeds and then just copy a file to one computer's serial port (from where it will go to the other's screen), this is a very limited way of doing things.

If the incoming file is too long to fit into the memory available, there needs to be some way of coordinating both computers so that everything is stopped while the memory contents are saved to disk and the rest is delivered properly. Usually, any communications program reserves a small space in memory (a *circular buffer*) where incoming or outgoing information is stored temporarily whilst everything is synchronised.

Conversations between devices to do with flow control are sometimes known as *handshaking*, and there are several systems to deal with this. Hardware handshaking, or the lack of it, is discussed under *RS232 Limitations*, below.

Xon/Xoff is one form of software handshaking that uses two special characters that are not (usually) used in ordinary text files, ASCII codes 17 (**Ctrl-Q**) and 19 (**Ctrl-S**), which mean *start* and *stop* transmitting respectively. These are sent with the data, but it's possible that a program file may contain either of the two as part of its operating code, and you can imagine the confusion that would cause if they were misinterpreted!

It works from *end-to-end*, which means between the extreme ends of the connection, or the computers concerned.

Xmodem, which is another handshaking method that doubles as a *file transfer protocol*, uses 8 bit words regardless. You will find this (and others) fully described in Chapter 10.

Connectors

These have already been mentioned in Chapter 3. At this stage, we only need to note that Pin 1, looking at the front of a female connector (the one with holes), is at the *top right*:

Pin 1

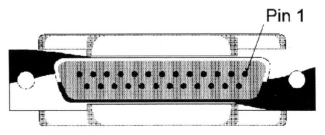

Pins

RS232 signals are numbered and named in accordance with three standard systems, plus another that isn't standard but in common use.

One is by pin number (used by most people) and another is by abbreviations of the signal description (that's the non-standard one, which we saw when looking at the modem lights). In describing the activities of the serial port, we will use both of these. The other two are boring, using technical definitions in the standards themselves.

Here's a full list of what every pin on the larger 25-pin connector is supposed to do:

1   **PG** *Protective Ground*. If used, this is for connecting the cable shielding to, but only at one end, to prevent spurious voltages between pin 7 and this one. If the two terminals are at different ground potentials, the resistance to current flow along wire 7 (which is a ground return path) could cause a potential difference between pins 1 and 7 at both ends. As *Potential Difference* is but another name for *Voltage*, it can be seen that it could be mistaken for a real signal. This is particularly important for terminals – it could stop them working at all.

2   **TD** *Transmit Data*. Signal names given are as viewed from the DTE (or computer), so data is transmitted *from* this pin *to* the DCE (modem).

3   **RD** *Receive Data*. As above, but in reverse, i.e. *to* the DTE.

4   **RTS** *Request To Send*. This is used to initialise the modem and goes *from* the DTE. Where half-duplex is used, this is also used to turn the direction of transmission around.

5   **CTS** *Clear To Send*. The modem's reply to the above.

6   **DSR** *Data Set Ready*. Indicates the modem's readiness for action (the term *Data Set*, meaning the modem, is an old American term used in the same way as *Radio Set*).

7   **SG** *Signal Ground*. The reference ground for all other signals, so it must be connected at both ends of the cable (but see also **Pin 1**).

8   **DCD** *Data Carrier Detect*. The modem activates this when it's happy with the quality of the telephone line.

9   **Data Set Test**.

10   **Data Set Test**.

11   **Unassigned**.

12   **SDCD** *Secondary DCD* (Pin 8). Sometimes used as a speed indicator where a modem senses it automatically. It goes *to* the DTE.

13   **SCTS** *Secondary CTS* (Pin 5).

14   **STD** *Secondary TD* (Pin 2).

15   **Transmit Clock** (for synchronous DCE operations).

16   **SRD** *Secondary RD* (pin 3).

17   **Receive Clock** (for synchronous DCE operations, but known to be used on some laptops for asynchronous chat with IBM PCs. It depends on the software).

18   **Unassigned**.

19   **SRTS** *Secondary RTS* (Pin 4.)

20   **DTR** *Data Terminal Ready* – *to* the modem.

21   **Signal Quality Detect** (synchronous operations).

22   **RI** *Ring Indicator*. How the modem tells the terminal that the phone is ringing (assuming an auto-answer capability). The current flows in sympathy with the ringing tone on the line.

23   **Data Signal Rate Select**. This is used whenever a modem is able to switch speeds.

24   **Transmit Clock** (for synchronous DTE operations, the same as pin 17).

25   **Unassigned**.

Wiring

The above pins fall into 3 distinct groups – data, control and timing. Pins 2-8 and 20 are the most relevant.

Data Pins

It's possible to get by with 2 (Tx), 3 (Rx) and 7 (Gd) when used at slow speeds. However, you may need others for flow control above 300 baud (having said that, some software used for file transfer between laptops and PCs, e.g. LapLink, use clever programming to get around this requirement, and still only use these three pins).

Control Pins

Pin 20, *Data Terminal Ready*, is used by the computer to tell the modem when it's ready for action, with a high voltage condition. Pin 6, *Data Set Ready*, is the complementary signal that says the modem is ready. If either goes low (or off) for any reason, then communications will stop.

If pin 20 is left on permanently, an auto-answer modem will answer immediately current is detected on pin 22 which, if you remember, flows in sympathy with the bell ringing. If not, when the modem detects ringing, it turns on pin 22 (RI) to indicate that it has done so. The computer responds by sending a signal on pin 20 to indicate Data Terminal Ready (DTR). The modem will then answer the phone.

When it detects the voltage level change which signifies the receiver being lifted, the terminal ringing in will turn on its pin 4 (RTS) which turns on the modem's transmitter. The answer CTS is given by the receiving modem on pin 5. On receipt of that, the calling modem will go on-line (either automatically or by being switched by the computer operator), which will cause it to produce its own tone.

When the receiving modem hears this, it informs its own terminal by turning on pin 8 (DCD) to indicate detection and capture of the complete line. Data will then flow up and down pins 2 and 3.

Data is not transmitted from the DTE (pin 2) unless the following 4 circuits are on (where they are implemented):

```
Pin 4      (RTS)
Pin 5      (CTS)
Pin 6      (DSR)
Pin 20     (DTR)
```

At the end of the session, the computer will turn off pin 4 (RTS), which in turn will cause its modem to stop its carrier signal. This makes the receiving computer drop pin 20, causing its modem to hangup. At this point pin 8 goes off, completing the whole sequence.

Otherwise, pins 12, 13, 14, 16 and 19 are secondary versions of all the above.

Timing Pins

Pins 15, 17, 21 and 24 are used for timing on synchronous modems (with occasional exceptions).

Secondary Pins

Secondary ones, when used, handle lower rates of data than the primary ones, but in the reverse direction. The officially unassigned pins are there for manufacturers' own preferences and for the operation of the cleverer modems.

9 pin vs 25

The difference between the 9- and 25-pin plugs is that the traditional function of pin 1 is left out and 22 is added (the Ring Indicator). Just for reference, here are the assignments for the 9-pin connector, with the 25-pin equivalents:

```
DB-9                                    DB-25 (V24)
1      DCD Data Carrier Detect 8
2      RD Receive Data               3
3      TD Transmit Data              2
4      DTR Data Terminal Ready 20
5      SG Signal Ground             7
6      DSR Data Set Ready          6
7      RTS Request To Send        4
8      CTS Clear To Send            5
9      RI Ring Indicator             22
```

And just in case you ever need it, here's one conversion between the two. It's valid where you want to connect a modem with a DB-25 to a computer with a DB-9 (but don't forget that male and female connectors need their wires connected to the proper pins):

```
DB-25                                DB-9

8     --------------------- 1
3     --------------------- 2
2     --------------------- 3
20    --------------------- 4
7     --------------------- 5
22    --------------------- 6
4     --------------------- 7
5     --------------------- 8
6     --------------------- 9
```

Null Modem Cables

If you connect one computer to another (both DTE), where does each find the DCE it requires in order to work properly?

Attaching anything other than a modem to an RS232 port involves fooling both pieces of equipment into thinking that there's a modem between them. Usually, this is done by rewiring the connection cable in such a way that it cancels the modem out, which is why it's called a null modem cable. One or two pins may also be shorted, but don't worry, no harm will be caused — part of the reasoning behind the standards was to establish voltage levels so that no damage would be caused to equipment (or people) if something was cross-wired by mistake.

All we need to do is find permutations of the eight mentioned above — 2 to 8 and 20 — that will convince both ends that they are talking through a modem. One of those we can eliminate straight away; number 7 (Ground Return), which is always constant. Next change round pins 2 and 3 so that the receiver of one end gets the transmitted data of the other. You could try transmitting with just these as, up to 300 baud, there would be very little handshaking needed.

However, this is a bare minumum, and only allows for XON/XOFF handshaking provided with software. To use higher speeds, you need at least five wires, so one type of null modem cable could have pins 4 and 5 crossed over the same way as 2 and 3. The same reversal should happen with 6 and 20 with 8 connected to them (short 6 and 8 together on each side):

```
 2  TD   --------\/--------   TD    2
 3  RD   --------/\--------   RD    3
 4  RTS  --------\/--------   RTS   4
 5  CTS  --------/\--------   CTS   5
 7  SG   ------------------   SG    7
 8  DCD  !                !   DCD   8
 6  DSR  !-------\/----- -!   DSR   6
20  DTR  --------/\--------   DTR  20
```

The reason for a short circuit here is nothing to do with control signals, but to allow a voltage from one pin to create a high condition on another; for example, a high voltage is needed on pin 8 to make it think that it's connected to an outside line. As this high voltage is not otherwise available unless this is the case, the same effect is usually achieved by connecting it to one of the handshaking wires (4, 5, 6 or 20) which will have something coming out of it near enough to what's required.

MS-DOS (and other software found on IBM types) uses BIOS calls to read the serial port (BIOS calls are special internal computer procedures) which were designed to refuse to send or receive unless there is a signal on the CTS, DSR and CD pins. Therefore, pins 4, 6 and 8 on a DB-25 or 1, 6 and 7 on a DB-9 should be connected to ensure the outgoing RTS signal is received back on them (actually, one is sufficient, and CD is really for modems anyway).

Sometimes you can feed back wires on the same port to get the same effect as crossing wires.

It helps first of all to know which way information is going along these pins. Viewed from the terminal, pin 4 (RTS) and pin 20 (DTR) *send* and pins 5 (CTS), 6 (DSR) and 8 (DCD) *receive*.

When the computer sends RTS (4), it expects a reply on CTS (5). If these pins are connected together, it will get its own signal back straight away and start sending. The same philosophy applies to DTR (20) and DSR (6), so joining these two will have a similar effect.

The arrangement below definitely works between a Victor Vicki and a Zenith 183 laptop (with a DB-9), though definitely not above 600 baud. That's about as weird as you can get!

```
 2  TD  --------\/-------- TD   2
 3  RD  --------/\-------- RD   3
 4  RTS ---!         !--- RTS  4
 6  DSR ---!         !--- DSR  6
 8  DCD ---!         !--- DCD  8
 5  CTS --------\/-------- CTS  5
20  DTR --------/\-------- DTR 20
```

RS232 Limitations

The RS232 and other standards only concern themselves with physical connections – they assume that anything else required for safe transmission is handled through software. As such, there is no *proper* flow control system (fast modems need flow control in their own right).

Flow Control

At first sight, you should be able to use the combination of RTS/CTS, as described above, but there are one or two problems. One is that the receiver is not allowed to stop sending *Clear To Send* (Pin 5) until the sender first drops *Request to Send* (Pin 4).

Although RTS and CTS are now used as hardware handshaking lines, they were meant to indicate other things than the fact that either end is ready to send or receive; they are actually intended to allow the DTE (computer) to request the DCE (modem) to hand over control of the whole line to it. Thus, the computer assumes that it has the line (bypassing the modem) for as long as it needs it and the receiver (in this case the modem) is not allowed to drop it just as it pleases, otherwise it would play havoc with the telephone lines (which was why the procedures were established in the first place).

The real handshaking in such circumstances is between the computer and the line, not between it and the modem, therefore RTS/CTS should not technically be used as flow control, although it is.

Cable Length

Aside from flow control, the principal problem with RS232 is its distance limitation of 50 feet at the highest data transfer rates.

This a technical limitation based on the voltages used in the interfaces, and can therefore be calculated. If lower speeds are used, the cable runs can be longer, but not by much. Without experimentation, there is always the danger of data being lost.

However, for normal single user communications, which are done either at very short (on the same desk) or long distances (over the telephone, where the real distance is only to the modem anyway), this is not really much of a disadvantage.

This is mostly something to watch out for when joining several computers together with the RS232 port, as mentioned in Chapter 23.

Transmission Speed

The maximum transmission speed is 20,000 bits per second.

Grounding methods

All the control and data signals are referenced against pin 7, which works satisfactorily most of the time. However, where there is a difference in ground potential between both ends of the cable (quite likely over a long run), then the difference between space and mark (or 0 or 1) is narrowed, giving more scope for misinterpretation.

Power Requirements

As the average PC was built for a single user, adding 20 or so serial ports on the back (with a multi I/O card on a comms server) could give it quite a shock!

Have a look at the -12v *maximum output current rating*, which supports the line drivers for the serial ports. As the -12v rating of most PC power supplies is in the order of .3-.5 amps, it may not be enough for what you want (although it's generally alright for small systems). As a worst case figure, expect to need about .4 amps for 20 terminals, 1 amp for 45, or 2 amps for 100, with cables attached.

If you're getting serial ports locking up or, more seriously, strange system reboots, you may well have an overloaded power supply (you're really in trouble if the system won't boot at all!).

Intelligent multi-port cards will have their own power supply.

Taken individually, the limitations described above seem not to be too troublesome, but if you try to drive cables that are too long at too high a speed, they may affect you all at once.

Other Standards

In order to overcome these limitations, the RS429, 422 and 423 standards have been designed to try and take care of the defects while applying basic improvements.

RS 449

This was intended to be a successor to RS232, with improved speed and distance specifications (50 feet) and modem testing; it makes reference to RS 422 and RS 423 as part of it. Unfortunately, it specifies a 37-pin connector for RS422 which, not surprisingly, meant that it wasn't taken up by anyone.

RS 422

To allow transmission at high data rates, RS422 uses two wires for each signal. This is called *balanced transmission* (as opposed to the RS232's *unbalanced transmission*, which uses one ground wire) and it doubles the number of wires in the cable, so some of the more esoteric functions of RS232 have been dropped (RI, secondary functions, etc) to make room. On the other hand, RS422 permits very high data transfer rates without the problems of varying ground potential.

Because of this, the tolerances allowed in the transition region between mark and space can be much closer; .4v instead of the 6v used in RS232.

These values therefore allow the use of the +/-5vpower supply commonly available in computers (RS232 transmitters generate voltages between +5 and +25 volts for space and -5 and -25 volts for mark — this means that an extra supply of power is required inside the computer to handle these as computers use +/-12 and +/-5v). See *Power Requirements*, above.

RS422 pins (as supplied on the Macintosh) are:

1	**PG** *Protective Ground*
2	**+5v** (reference only)
3	**SG** *Signal Ground*
4	**TD+** *Transmit Data* (positive voltage)
5	**TD-** *Transmit Data* (negative voltage)
6	**+12v** (reference only)
7	**Handshake**
8	**RD+** *Receive Data* (positive voltage)
9	**RD-** *Receive Data* (negative voltage)

The cable length and data rate are related, in that the data rate multiplied by the cable length must be lower than 120 Mbps multiplied by metres, subject to the maximum data rate of 10 Mbps over 1200m (4000 feet).

```
MAC (DIN-8) to RS422:

Pin  DIN-8              DB-9
1    Handshake, output  HSKo (+12v)
2    Handshake, input   HSKi
3    Transmit Data—     TD—(negative)
4    Protective ground  PG
5    Receive Data—      RD—(negative)
6    Transmit Data +    TD—(positive)
7    Not connected
8    Receive Data  +    RD—(positive)
```

```
MAC (DIN-8) to Modem DB-25

DIN-8                              DB-25
4     PG  ------------ SG          7
3     TD  ------------ TD          2
5     RD  ------------ RD          3
1     HSKo ----------- DTR         20
2     HSKi ----------- CTS         5
```

RS 423

RS423 transmits in unbalanced fashion at lower speeds than RS422 and again uses a common return path for signals in a given direction, so it has two one-way return paths.

This standard operates in both RS232 and 422A environments and can act as a bridge between the two, as RS422A transmitters will not drive 232 receivers correctly because of the smaller transition region between space and mark.

There must be a 4v voltage difference (plus or minus) between the signals in RS423A, thus giving an 8v transition region which is compatible with RS232. However, this does present the same power supply problem.

RS 530

Essentially, RS422 using a 25-pin connector.

9

Software

There are two types of system you are likely to connect to; those with a *scrolling display* (like your normal screen) and those with *Viewdata*. Viewdata, used extensively in Europe, combines text with basic colour and graphics to give the sort of display used by Prestel, travel agents and Teletext. It's not supported by American software.

The point about software is *automation*; that is, you should be able to get it to do most of the work; once you tell it what sort of modem you have, it should send all the right signals for you. For this, there ought to be an element of programmability, in the shape of a *scripting language* (macros, really) that should at least issue your ID and password when you log on.

In most cases, though, automation will stop at that point, unless you go quite deeply into scripting. Unfortunately, there's not enough time in the day for all that as well, so there are two types of program that will bridge the gap, which are specific to their particular systems. The objective of both is the same; to make using On-Line services considerably easier and quicker, thus reducing phone bills, but they do it in different ways.

- An **On-Line Reader** issues complicated commands on your behalf, so where you would normally issue about three lines of gibberish to see what files are available for downloading, you might be able to choose them from a nice looking menu instead. In short, it helps you move around the system while on-line.

- An **Off-Line Reader** does the same, but you're only connected long enough to send and receive messages you prepared earlier; all your messages are uploaded and downloaded by the program automatically, as are lists of files available, so you can browse through them at your leisure. The next time you log on everything is done without you touching a thing. It types a lot faster than you can, and doesn't make any mistakes!

What to look for

For PCs, products fall into two camps, for Windows and DOS. Performance can be better with the latter, because there is more scope for taking shortcuts with programming, but it really depends on many factors.

These features make a well-rounded software package:

- **Serial port configuration** without you touching the system setup commands.

- **Preconfigured setup routines** initialisation strings for the most popular modems.

- **Redirection of input** or output to where it's required.

- **Terminal emulation**, or pretending to be equipment that the computer at the other end can recognise. A terminal is used by some large computers to talk to the outside world, having a screen and keyboard only.

    There are several types, none of which behave like an IBM-compatible computer or a Mac, hence the need for translation. VT-100 is a common choice, but TTY, ANSI and PRESTEL are others. You need to set the terminal type so that your keystrokes can be interpreted correctly and the right characters shown on the screen. Your keyboard may change its behaviour according to how the keyboard is mapped.

- **Telephone directory**, for commonly used numbers, and the linking of scripts thereto. These should be exchangeable with other programs (saves typing!).

- **MNP**, so older modems without it can be used.

- **Protocols**, in the shape of ZModem and Kermit at least.

- **Scripting language**.

- **Decent Manual**.

- **16550 support** (it has to be activated with software).

- **Good text editor**, so you can compose your messages easily.

Setting Up

You obviously need to know what settings the receiving computer expects, so you can to talk to it properly; luckily, speed detection on Bulletin Boards is usually automatic, and many modems can start at a high speed and work downwards (i.e. *fall back*) to a slower one until you're connected, so maybe try 9600 first.

You will need to know which COMmunications port your modem is attached to. A PC usually has two of these, COM1 and COM2, where COM1 is commonly taken up by a mouse, just to make things awkward. If you're not sure, try each one in turn. If your computer freezes up, the COM port you have chosen is already in use by another piece of equipment.

Your software needs to control your hardware in terms of:

- **Speed**, or the number of data bits transferred per second. Typical speeds range from 300 to 9600 bps, but the telephone lines are not capable of handling more than 2400 on average without squeezing more bits per baud.

  With data compression, you can often get an *effective speed* higher than your modem would normally allow. You can connect at 38,400 bps with a 14,400 bps modem, if you use V.42*bis* at each end.

- **Parity**, which is a primitive form of error checking, and more or less out of date, so it's usually set to None (the other options are Even and Odd).

- **Data bits**; that is, the number of bits transferred at a time. If you remember, a byte consists of eight bits. If you use Even or Odd parity (above), the eighth bit will be used for error checking, which reduces the chances of transmitting complex characters.

- **Stop bits**. Because only one cable is used to transmit data, there needs to be some way of telling when each character sent comes to an end, which is what a stop bit is for. It's simply an extra bit that is immediately recognisable as not being a character, so the computer knows when the next one starts. If you like, stop bits are there to give the computers a chance to synchronise with each other. Usually set to 1.

- **Handshaking**, or how the flow of data between each computer is to be controlled (that is, concerning the hardware only). There must be a way, for example, for the receiving computer to tell the sending one to stop for a while if it gets a problem. Usually, this will be CTS/RTS. Don't use XON/XOFF.

- **Protocol**, which is similar to handshaking, but for use between programs (hardware-based handshaking is a personal matter between the computers). The best general choices are ZMODEM, YMODEM, XMODEM or ASCII, in that order, but see Chapter 10.

- **Type of dialling** (Tone/Pulse).

All of the above settings can be set from within your communications software, usually at the same time as setting up the telephone number of the computer you want to talk to (look for *Settings....*).

Modem settings

A non-Hayes modem, that is, one that is compatible but not made by Hayes, sometimes needs to be told to use a *reduced command set*.

MODE

Normally, your software sets up the serial port, but you could do it manually. The MS-DOS program that allows you to do this is called MODE.COM which, in addition to allowing you to alter the serial port settings, also allows you to fiddle around with the parallel port or the monitor. These are not our concern, though.

As far as the serial port is concerned, MODE sets up the baud rate, parity and number of data and stop bits used by information passing through either COM1 or COM2.

A typical command will look like this:

```
MODE COM1:300,E,8,1
```

where COM1 has been set to 300 baud with even parity, eight data bits and one stop bit, in that order.

To change anything, just alter the information between the commas (in the right sequence) or omit it, but you must still supply a separating comma if what you've missed out is in the middle – check out:

```
MODE COM2:12,,7
```

where COM2 has been set to 1200 baud and seven data bits while the rest has been set to the default values of even parity and 1 stop bit (2 stop bits if 110 baud is used). The default number of data bits is 7. A baud rate must be specified every time, but you only need to supply the first two figures.

To use the MODE command to redirect the printer output to the serial port (after the rest has been done), use:

```
MODE LPT1(2 or 3): = COM1(or 2)
```

STAT

The STAT command is used in CP/M mainly for checking on the status of various parts of the computer, such as the disk drives and the files on them. However, it can also carry out similar functions to MODE in MS-DOS, except that it doesn't set up the parameters of the port you're using (that's usually done with a CONFIGURE or SETUP program).

What it does do, though, is allow you to redirect output to one part of the computer or another (if you've got a dead printer, check that you're sending data to the right port). CP/M always puts information out through four possible outlets, but we're only interested in what it calls a LIST Device (a printer, in English) or the CONsole.

For instance, you could redirect what would normally go to the screen (CONsole) to the printer port, or vice versa. Just because a device is called LIST Device, the output doesn't actually have to go to one — you could actually send it to a modem that's occupying the space where the program thinks the printer should be. Provided the operating characteristics are the same, there should be no trouble.

This is all the program needs to look for, since CP/M takes the output and moves it to the real one. In other words, a program will look for a notional list device (i.e. it doesn't really exist), but CP/M will put it out to where it should be. This gives you some flexibility, as a program can remain standard for various machines, and all you do is call a device something else so that the program thinks that what it's talking to. You can tell CP/M that whenever List Device is referred to by a program, what it really means is whatever you specify with STAT.

One major difference between CP/M and MS-DOS is that the command syntax is usually back to front, and STAT is no exception.

For instance, to redirect output to the equivalent of COM1, say:

```
STAT LST:=UL1
```

which really means that "the status of the list device is equal to User List 1", or in other words "the list device is now COM1", if you were doing the same thing in DOS. If you recall your algebra and replace STAT with LET, it becomes easier – what you're saying is LET the List Device (LST:) equal User Port 1 (UL1).

Remote Control (Teleworking)

If you use a computer at home as well as at work, there will no doubt come a day when you need to get information from the office and can't be bothered to drive there – maybe you need to support people in the field, such as salesmen.

There is software specially made for remote access like this, such as *pcAnywhere*, *CO/Session* or *Carbon Copy* (there are others). They load a memory resident program that watches for modem activity.

When the other half of the software rings in, it passes control over and you can operate the remote computer as if you were sitting at its keyboard. Note that no data is being transferred, only screen and keyboard information, so your PC at home is behaving like a terminal.

2400 baud is about the lowest acceptable speed for DOS programs, but obviously the faster the better. Just don't expect graphics!

See also *Internetworking*, Chapter 18.

10

File Transfer

There are two types of data that can be sent between computers; ASCII or Binary, and it's important to tell your software which one it's dealing with.

ASCII

The problem with data files saved in the format of the program that produced them is that "real" Carriage Returns are only found at the end of each paragraph. At the end of every other line is a *soft return*, which is put there by the word wrap procedure when it puts the text on the next line automatically. Naturally, different programs have different ways of doing this, so confusion reigns if no particular standards are used, which is where ASCII comes in as a lowest common denominator for the exchange of data between programs.

The term "ASCII" is often synonymous with "text", as an ASCII file contains no formatting instructions, such as where to start bold or italic printing, where the tabs are, and the like; in other words, there are no hidden codes put there by the software; there's also a Carriage Return and Line Feed at the end of each line. Thus "ASCII file" = "text file".

It's not safe to assume that conversion to ASCII is done automatically when data is sent, so you *must convert it before you send it*.

Binary Files

These are files consisting of program code. If they're not given special treatment, the odd byte in them may be misinterpreted as an instruction at either end and thoroughly confuse the whole issue.

The classic example is the command sometimes used to denote the end of a text file, which is ⌃ Z (**Ctrl-Z**). This can appear in a program file in an entirely different context, but will be taken to mean the end of the file, and the one you are transmitting will be cut short in its prime.

Protocols

A file, as you already know, is a block of data that is addressed as a whole, usually by name. Transferring files is process that takes the whole file and moves it to somewhere else *undamaged*, and a protocol makes this possible.

A protocol can operate where the timing and sequencing of events is unknown and errors in transmission are expected, so it has quite a bit of work to do. It must inform the devices involved as to whether they are source or destination and identify the files involved. It must also establish whether the file will be stored anew or attached to an existing one.

The key elements of a protocol are *syntax* (concerning the format of the signals and their levels), *semantics* (information needed for communications) and *timing* (the speeds for the matching and sequencing of events). They send data in packets because they're easier to resend than whole files.

A *streaming protocol* doesn't wait for "correct receive" acknowledgements, but sends continually and aborts transmission if an error is detected (on the receiving side). This is useful where error correction is handled by other means, such as a modem using MNP or V.42, so streaming protocols are faster, because they do no error checking. They should be avoided unless your connections are 100%.

A protocol's *window* concerns the amount of blocks sent at a time without acknowledgements; a window of 4 means 4 at a time.

Following is a list of the most common you may encounter, but a lot of them are programs in their own right. Note that your choice will depend on several things, not least the quality of the phone lines. Most are only capable of half-duplex, where transmission only takes place in one direction at a time.

ASCII

Starting with the basics, *ASCII transfer* simply means the process of typing characters and the receiver accepting them into memory – in other words, similar to a telex or teleprinter. There is no error detection, and it's difficult to save to disk.

What's called *ASCII file transfer* just about makes it as a protocol, as it only uses Xon/Xoff handshaking. Only use 7 data bits with this.

HS-Link

A bidirectional protocol which can be used just about anywhere, including networks. Used when you need to send files in both directions at the same time.

Compuserve B+

A proprietary protocol used by Compuserve, which initiates data transfers by itself. Always use this when talking to Compuserve.

XModem

The original modem transfer protocol (written by Ward Christensen in 1977), which started as MODEM2 on CP/M, devised as a simple 8-bit error checking scheme suitable for use between computers. As it's eight-bit, you can't use XON/XOFF, so you must either not need flow control, or have it hardware-based. Xmodem splits data up into 128 byte blocks and uses a checksum for error checking.

The sending machine launches the first block on receipt of a Negative Acknowledge (NAK) character from the receiving terminal (they are sent out every 10 seconds when in a waiting state).

When the block arrives, the receiver checks the message by making sure that it has a Start Of Header character at the front, that the block number is the next in sequence to the last one received, that 128 characters actually were there and that the checksum at the end tallies with the locally computed one. If it's happy with that, it sends an *acknowledge* signal (06 hex) to the sender, which sends the next block when that is received.

If it isn't happy, then a NAK is sent and the block is retransmitted. An *End of Text* character is sent at the end of the complete message.

The simplicity of Xmodem is also its main drawback, in that it's unable to detect noise bursts that are able to take out 12 or more bits at a go. Like Kermit (see below), it also requires one terminal to be identified as a sender and the other as a receiver, so a terminal is needed at each end with the setup being done manually (that can be a bit awkward at times).

It's also inefficient in its use of the line, in that it needs full duplex facilities to operate a half-duplex service, as it sends information on one line and waits for an acknowledgement on another (it can't hand over control of any lines to the other machine). The line can be idle for relatively long periods.

Another problem is that it can transfer only one file at a time and the filename must be entered explicitly, with no wildcards.

Xmodem usually cannot be used over networks, multiplexed connections or X.25 circuits, because of the control characters it uses. It doesn't have a configurable block size and it alters the size of files, rounding them up to the nearest 128 bytes, the block size it uses (a CP/M limitation, this). Neither does it perform data compression.

Only use Xmodem when nothing else works.

XModem-CRC

As above, but uses a 16-bit CRC, so it's less likely to miss multiple errors, although it is marginally slower.

Relaxed XModem

Used when certain hosts can't maintain the strict timing Xmodem needs. It simply multiplies the timing by a factor of ten; for instance, where Xmodem might wait 2 seconds for a character, Relaxed Xmodem will wait for 20.

Xmodem-1K

Sometimes confused with YModem; Xmodem with 1K blocks.

YModem

As for Xmodem-CRC, except that block sizes of 1 K are supported, and file names and lengths are sent along in a block before the data, so the receiver knows what size of file to expect. YModem was developed under CP/M by Chuck Forsberg as YAM, but by the time it got to PCs in 1981 had become an improvement on Xmodem. Be aware that not all Ymodems you get are the same; it might handle more than one file at once, but you may only get to send one at a time — see *YModem Batch*.

Use when the phone lines are good to fair.

Ymodem Batch

"Batch" means you can send more than one file at a time, and you can use wildcard characters for multiple files. Although the batch facility is part of YModem, this is sometimes implemented as a separate protocol.

YModem-G

Sends data in 1K blocks as a continuous stream, with no error checking (it leaves this to hardware), so is a streaming protocol as fast as ZMODEM (below). Use with error-corrected links, or when the phone lines are good.

YModem-G Batch

As above, but can handle multiple file names.

IModem

Developed by John Friel. It performs no error checking, so only use when the phone lines are good.

WXModem

Developed by Peter Boswell as a Full Duplex sliding window protocol that can send up to four Xmodem blocks before needing an acknowledgement. Can handle network flow control.

ZModem

Another creation of Chuck Forsberg, written in 1986. It can automatically set the receiving station into receive mode when the first data blocks arrive. Most hosts supporting this offer automatic transfer initiation.

32-bit CRCS are used, but no checking takes place or corrections performed until the whole file has been transmitted.

Zmodem is a streaming window protocol, but doesn't abort the transmission process if there's a mistake; instead, it just asks for a retransmission. Block sizes are automatically varied according to error rates; the more errors are reported, the smaller the block size becomes. Best of all, it remembers where it left off, so it can even recover from aborted transfers (days later), or if you're using a satellite link.

It is fast, except with static, so use when the phone lines are good.

JModem

A high-speed variation of Xmodem.

SEALink

This is a version of WXmodem, with a window of 6, developed by Thom Henderson of *System Enhancement Associates*.

It's a *sliding window protocol*, which basically means that unless an error is detected, data is sent constantly with no pauses. Because of this, SEAlink is very fast – 15-25% faster than Xmodem, which makes it better for packet switched networks and satellite link-ups where delays are common in the system anyway; it can send up to six 128-byte blocks before requiring an acknowledgement. SEAlink passes a file's name, size and date when transferring it, and can be used in batch mode.

Telink

Telink, from Tom Jennings, is mainly found on Fido Bulletin Boards as it's commonly used with them. It's basically Xmodem, but also compatible with Modem7 (below) using CRC checking with an extra block sent behind the file name, but ahead of the file itself, containing its vital statistics, such as file size and creation date (for MS-DOS), so you don't get padded files. Again, this is a batch protocol, and you can use wildcards.

Modem7

A close cousin of Xmodem (using the same protocol, anyway) that passes the filename before starting the transfer, thus taking away some of the work – you don't need to waste time telling the receiver what it's getting.

It's available on almost all CP/M and MS-DOS machines. Modem7-compatible programs can transfer one or more files at a time, with full error-detection and correction.

The main limitation under MS-DOS is that the original file creation time and exact file size are lost (but check out Telink above).

Mex

*M*odem *EX*ecutive, to give its full name, is a derivative of Modem7 used mainly with CP/M.

Kermit

The Kermit protocol is in a class of its own and has special features that warrant giving it further attention. For one thing, it's available for just about every computer that exists, and acts as a lowest common denominator, so don't expect graphics or other fancy features (it can use 7-or 8-bit ASCII, so is good with mainframes that can only cope with 7-bit). There is also a sliding windows version that uses Full Duplex (i.e. you can send data continuously and get replies at the same time), and you can use Kermit when the lines are terrible.

Kermit has a limited terminal emulation facility which allows you to be a slave terminal to a mainframe.

Actually, Kermit is both a program in its own right and a protocol that has been incorporated into many other programs, in which case it will be much faster than the original.

It's in the Public Domain, which means that the copyright remains with the author (Frank de Cruz/Columbia University in the USA) and the program may not be sold or altered without their written permission (the UK equivalent to Columbia University is the University of Lancaster, from where copies may also be obtained). You can freely copy it, give it away or whatever, as long as you don't charge for the software or anything based on its code.

Thus, any charges you may get involved with should only be for the cost of the media used to carry it; not much more than the price of a disk and postage.

For a Public Domain program, the support and documentation is very good. The trouble is there's so much of it (the text file that comes on disk is 290 Kbytes long, takes ages to print out and uses a stack of paper), and if all you're using is a small PC, you don't need much of that at all to be effective. Like all things, if you know why you're doing something, sometimes you don't need instructions at all, so assuming you have the main program (KERMIT.EXE for an IBM), let's look at what's behind it all.

Kermit works by converting the data coming from either terminal into its own codes, and reconverting it at the other end. Like everything else, it splits the information up and sends it in packets of a particular size (say 128 bytes) with control information added, such as a marker for synchronisation of the transmission itself and a sequence number in case a packet gets lost.

Its particular strength is its error checking protocols. A length indicator and a "block check" are provided for detecting errors, but one slight problem is that if the last bit of data is not enough to fill a packet, Kermit will pad the rest out, like XModem does. To change this so that the end of the file is actually marked at the end of the data, you need to use the **SET EOF** (SET END-OF-FILE) command, which is explained later.

Speeds and other parameters should be correct at either end, and once inside the program you can check what the settings are by typing, **STATUS**, which will provide a complete list of the default values your particular version has.

On most versions, you can set everything you need to from within the program, but this can be time consuming if you use it on a regular basis for the same thing. You can't do this at all with some machines, notably CP/M ones, where you have to set everything up *before* you invoke Kermit — see also the section on the MODE and STAT commands at the end of Chapter 9.

To have Kermit start up with your favourite default values, you need to make up an ASCII file called MSKERMIT.INI (for MS-DOS computers, but check for your own make — and whatever it is, it needs to be in the same directory path as the main program) into which Kermit looks on start-up so it can set itself up how you want.

This file is merely a list of all the commands that indicate your personal preferences, each on a separate line, like those given below.

```
set baud 300
set parity even
```

To start the program, type:

```
KERMIT
```

at the system prompt (or *KERMIT on a BBC) and the computer will respond with something like this:

```
KERMIT>
```

This prompt can be customised, but that's a bit esoteric for us — in other words, you'll have to look up the proper reference manual for how to do it, as well as for the editing commands!

If you need it at any stage, Help is readily available by typing ?, and it's (sort of) case-specific. Usually it just consists of a list of available commands (what do you expect for free?).

Once inside the program, commonly used commands include:

SET	A parameter, such as SET BAUD 300
SHOW	A parameter, such as SHOW BAUD
STATUS	Enquiry about settings
SPACE	Enquiry about disk space
DIRECTORY	List of files on disk

SEND	File to other Kermit (add the name)
RECEIVE	File from other Kermit (add the name)
CONNECT	To a remote system (E-mail, etc)
SERVER	Makes other terminal obey your Kermit
GET	File from remote server
FINISH	Shut down remote server
BYE	Disconnect from remote system
EXIT	From Kermit (or QUIT)
HANGUP	The phone

Most of these (I hope) are self explanatory, if a little cryptic. There are other commands which will be shown by invoking HELP. All of these are LOCAL, meaning that they refer to your terminal.

However, by prefixing them with REMOTE, the same commands can be made to operate on another computer running Kermit which must previously have been designated as a SERVER (when doing this, use the prefix LOCAL with the above commands to avoid confusion).

Kermit File Transfer

In principle, this is simple. Well, at least it is if the computers are on the same desk, in which case all you need to do is get Kermit up and running at the right speed on both machines, tell one to RECEIVE the FILE you want and then the other to SEND the same FILE and voila! Kermit will transmit everything, checking for errors on the way.

In practice, however, there are one or two things that you may want to sort out before you start. For instance, some versions of Kermit like to know if they are sending ASCII or Binary files (not with MS-DOS), so you tell it before you start by saying SET FILE-MODE ASCII (or BINARY). Some Kermits may need files translated to 7-bit ASCII because of the formatting commands included in 8-bit ASCII by some MS-DOS programs.

Also, certain MS-DOS programs (like CP/M ones) terminate a file with **Ctrl-Z**, which will cause things to hang if that command isn't present. Kermit has a SET EOF (Set End-Of-File) command that caters for this (again, see later).

Actually, it's not strictly necessary to specify the filename for receiving unless you want to change it — Kermit will save it under the filename sent by the other end, and will even alter incoming filenames if there are illegal characters, or one with the same name already.

However, just to show Kermit's versatility, all of the above procedures can be done over the telephone lines from a remote computer with everything being controlled from your terminal. Kermit has to be running on both machines, of course, but you can even start the other one from yours — here's how:

Get Kermit running by using the procedure above and SET the parameters you require.

Now type:

    CONNECT

(C will do just as well), followed by RETURN. Take a note of the Escape character shown on the screen (this can also be customised if you want), because this will allow you to regain control from your terminal later.

Once everything is connected, your computer will become a dumb terminal of the other one, in which case you may need to enter IDs, Passwords and the like to make it recognise your existence (on the IBM PC, Kermit provides an almost complete emulation of the DEC VT-102 terminal at speeds of up to 19,200 baud. This terminal emulation can be changed to something else, if required, through the program). It is important to appreciate that you are *not in native Kermit mode* at the moment.

All you need then do is type KERMIT, prefixed by whatever command is needed to run any program (such as R on a DEC mainframe, so you need R Kermit) and the program should start, showing you a similar system prompt to yours.

You can either tell the other Kermit to SEND the FILE you want and while it's getting ready to do that, quickly ESCAPE back to yours (using the code) to RECEIVE it (or vice versa), or just reverse the two computers' roles — type SERVER and with the use of the escape code you will be back in charge of your machine and talking to your Kermit with the remote machine serving your Master, shown by the appearance of your system prompt (that is, assuming the other Kermit allows SERVER operation).

The use of the SERVER mode is quite useful as the use of a SEND command from you automatically invokes a RECEIVE command at the other end (or alternatively, a one-stroke method of getting the remote machine to send a file is just to use GET, followed by the filename you want, but this is only available for Server operation).

Once file transfer is in operation, the screen should change and a small table will appear showing the name of the file to be transmitted (resist pressing the Return key or otherwise trying to get some action while transfer commences, as it does take a few seconds).

Depending on your version of Kermit, you may be shown progressively the percentage transferred so far and to go, the number of kilobytes sent successfully, the number of packets sent and the number of retries.

A tip is to watch the retries—if there are lots, then check that the baud rate's not too high and the physical connections are OK.

Electronic Mail with Kermit

Using the same principles shown above, it's possible to log on to an Electronic Mail service using Kermit as the communications program. Again, start the program, set up the parameters and type CONNECT.

Kermit should then take command of the modem (shown by the DTR light coming on) and show you an empty screen for your commands—you're in terminal mode here. You will have to log on manually but, then again, Kermit's free.

NOTES

11

Bulletin Boards

A Bulletin Board is the electronic equivalent of a public noticeboard, where anybody suitably equipped with a modem and a computer can place or read messages. Some allow you to send and receive mail, or have areas (*forums*) for special interest groups, such as the local river-wideners club. Others allow you to chat on-line, or download any software they allow you to get your hands on.

In short, they are the equivalent of commercial E-Mail services but privately run by amateurs, similar to radio hams (the word amateur here is not meant to mean "unprofessional", but "enthusiastic").

The first Bulletin Boards appeared in the late 70s, but were limited, in that only one person at at time could logon and use their facilities.

There could be several reasons for a Bulletin Board being in existence. Many companies establish them for customer or field engineer support, which may include ordering facilities. Even local authorities have them.

Although large companies can run Bulletin Boards as cheap E-Mail and conferencing systems, here we are mainly concerned with the smaller ones generally run on a non-profit making basis by a lone enthusiast using a micro and modem – in other words with minimal equipment (actually, some of it is not so minimal).

There is a form of etiquette attached to Bulletin Boards. As you're not paying for the service, you shouldn't abuse it, which means treating all concerned with respect and courtesy (assuming you get it in the first place, of course!). Obscene messages left lying around are not popular! Log on with care, be brief and read the "new user" messages that may be around, usually in the *Bulletins* section.

You shouldn't hog the download facilities, and why not occasionally upload a Public Domain program you've found useful?

Logging on is quite simple. Most modems can start with a high speed and work downwards from that (known as *falling back*). The number of stop bits is usually 1, number of data bits 8 and parity none.

There may be a *ringback system*, which is used when the BBS has only one line and the computer counts a ringback call as being intended for its use. Allow the phone to ring a couple of times, and if there's no answer, hang up and ring back (hence the name). If the modem answers, on the other hand, just go on-line.

Once you're in, you will be asked for your first and last names, together with some information about your equipment, and be invited to register as a user (again, courtesy demands that you don't give them false details). You will need a password for future occasions so others can't pretend to be you, so have one ready. Usually, everything is organised by menus, so it will be quite easy to find your way around. There may be some instruction files you can download and read at your leisure, which will save you tying up the system while you find your way around (look under *Bulletins*).

You will find that many boards have the same basic layout and menus, mainly because they use the same software.

Sometimes boards go off-line for various reasons — Fido boards (see later) go off and talk amongst themselves at some unearthly hour of the morning (about 0230), linking up and transmitting messages to each other.

When you have to go, it isn't good manners just to drop the line when you get fed up (in fact, it's never a good idea to do it at any time with any program), so leave by the routes provided, otherwise the system could take some time to reorganise itself.

Leave a thank-you message or some constructive criticism for the person who runs the board (who is known as the SYSOP, by the way, short for SYStem OPerator). It's his job to maintain things, register users, back things up and generally to maintain security.

Networking BBSs

FidoNet was developed in America to allow users to read mail on other boards. It started because the authors of the Fido BBS software needed to exchange modifications to their code on opposite sides of the country. They designed a system where the board would shut down as a nightly event and run utilities that exchanged data back and forth. The utilities gradually became part of the BBS package itself.

Put simply, FidoNet is a collection of Bulletin Boards that connect together for the purposes of sharing mail. The name comes from the fact that they originally used the same software (FIDO), but now anything compatible can join in.

Mail sent this way is known as *EchoMail*, so if you see a reference to it, you know that your message will be sent to other systems in the network, at the previously mentioned unearthly hour in the morning (actually, the times are allocated by a coordinator).

Each FidoNet has a central node (any BBS on the system), called the Hub, which collects and distributes any mail throughout the BBSs in its area.

PCRelay does the same as Fido, but in a different way, using a different topology through third party comms programs, such as *Telix* or *ProComm Plus*.

Starting your own Bulletin Board

Before you do, it's only polite to your potential users to run one that's viable in the first place. The etiquette goes both ways — it's not fair to get them to log on and waste their phone bills while you muck around not knowing what you're doing! The viability of what you propose depends mainly on cost and the time you have available to run things.

The hardware

A Bulletin Board can be very inexpensive to set up. The easiest way is just to rent space in one of the commercial systems, but otherwise all you need is a single computer with a disk drive (a hard disk is best), one or more serial ports, an auto-answer modem (Hayes compatible, preferably, with auto baud-rate scanning), a telephone line and some controlling software.

For small scale boards, BBCs still have a strong following in some areas of the country, and the Atari ST can do a respectable job with just two 1 Mb floppy drives, which just goes to prove something, but I'm not sure what.

As a result, the whole lot could set you back less than £1500 (depending on the equipment used), without allowing for your own time to set the thing up, and the phone lines. The costs per line will naturally drop in relation to the number of lines added.

Running costs of course will consist of electricity, telephone rental, backup media and time for maintenance — you'll need to take it off line sometimes to delete old messages, answer callers' questions and make general improvements as things go on.

Concerning your time, allow about 120 hours learning how to set it all up and 10 hours per week maintenance.

One or two operating problems may arise that could soak up even more of your time and money. If your board becomes popular, you will need fast and effective backup systems, such as tape streamers and the like. You will find that a 1 Gb hard disk won't last long in terms of space, especially as you can't claim all of it – you will need some disk space constantly free for uploads and workspace. This will mean a lot of weeding to get rid of unwanted files, which takes time.

Also, if you live in a built-up area, you will have to watch the power supplies during the adverts on TV as half the neighbourhood gets up to put the kettle on. You may feel the need of an *uninterruptible power supply* to keep things going if this happens (see Chapter 9 for more about these).

A dedicated telephone line (not a real one, only in the sense of just being used for the computer) is almost a must, though some Boards are run by people telephoning in and asking the SysOp to plug in the modem! The main reason for having a dedicated line is that people will always call outside any published operating hours and may not realise that you have answered the phone and not your equipment – unless you like your ears punished by modem tones, of course!

BBS Software

As with anything, get the software first, then the hardware to fit. The software will be determined by your reason for starting the BBS in the first place – will it be a full-blown E-Mail system allowing interaction from callers, or will it be read-only? Different software has different strengths and weaknesses, but it will certainly need to be able to handle multiple tasks and users with a registration system for checking passwords and suchlike.

In its most basic form, the software will run on a dedicated PC with one modem attached to it. At the other extreme, there may be 250 lines, allowing more users at any time to participate. Core facilities include leaving public messages for as many people to read as possible, or private messages for individuals. Also, it needs to be able to accept incoming files and to send files to callers (uploading and downloading).

On the PC, names to look out for include: The Major BBS, Maximus CBCS, Oracomm-Plus, PCBoard, RBBS-PC, Remote Access, Searchlight, Spitfire, Opus, TBBS and Wildcat!, although these are by no means the only ones.

For the Atari, try Michtron's BBS, which is reported to be quite user-friendly. If you're more experienced, try FoReM ST from America which is more complicated.

One way to find out what's good or not is to ask the SysOps of various operational systems and see what they think of theirs (if the SysOp is an enthusiast, he may well think his software is the best for everything, so you may have to read between the lines a bit).

When designing your menus, and the way people progress round the system, keep things consistent – that is, always use the same keys to back up through the system. Again, note the things you like and don't like about other peoples' systems.

Security

The biggest problem with running a bulletin board is security. If you're using a Hayes-type modem, the escape codes needed to revert to the command state can be accomplished by a remote computer just as much as yours. If they can do that with a modem, think what they can do if they can get a Format command through to your computer!

Also, any modems that store numbers and passwords are liable to picked clean by any hacker worthy of the name, so give some thought to storing these in your computer instead (that's why you need software that has password facilities).

Packet Radio

This is an extension to the Bulletin Board idea which uses principles from packet switching, so it combines computers and radio systems into a full-blown communications system all on its own. The thing most in common with Bulletin Boards is the attitude of the people involved – those who set it up go into it for the fun and the challenge, although they can be used in business for hand held data entry round supermarkets, for instance.

Even the standards are the same or very similar, the AX.25 packet structure used on the system being highly equivalent to the X.25 standards used for normal packet systems.

You need a different type of modem, though. This is because no start and stop signals are sent to indicate the beginning and end of transmission. Modems that support the +W extension to the Hayes standard are what to look for.

Using Packet Radio means that you don't need to join PSS and get charged to use the system; you can do the same over the air for a very small annual charge (however, you do need to pass the Radio Amateur's Licence). Also, you can use the many PBBSs (Packet Bulletin Boards) without the added complications of the phone bill.

Ordinary comms programs can be used – after all, they only concern themselves with data going in and out of the RS232 port. Where it goes or comes from beyond that is not relevant to them, provided the protocols are the same at both ends.

The only big difference is that you can't get Duplex operations the same as you can on the telephone – it's Half Duplex only. In addition, there's not the security you would expect with anything else as everyone monitors the net, but it is a matter of courtesy not to tamper with other peoples' messages.

Software to look out for to get you started is YAPP (amongst several others), which stands for Yet Another Packet Program and only works with IBM-type machines.

If you're interested, you can get more information from either the British Amateur Radio Teleprinter Group at Ffynnonias, Salem, Llandeilo, Dyfed SA19 7NP or the Radio Society of Great Britain, Lambda House, Cranbourne Rd, Potters Bar, Herts EN6 3JE.

12

The Internet

The Internet is a patchwork of computer networks initially set up in the USA to carry E-mail between universities, government agencies, the military and the occasional large company, which is now a worldwide public and commercial network, more or less out of control. The idea was to link together information resources and to exchange data between them on an informal basis; it's not an organisation to which you pay a subscription to join directly, but if you ever wondered where the global village was, this is it, with the Internet as a dirt track leading to the Information Superhighway!

The networks it is made up of are established for their own reasons, but the owners share their facilities, including files and message passing, for the benefit of others.

It grew out of a system which linked four Universities in California to the University of Utah, and which was designed to run if links were lost or added at random (as they would be in a nuclear war), so it assumes that no link is reliable; if one goes, the others take the strain. Message packets are treated as being entirely different from any other, and routed according to congestion.

Data transfer was the original idea, but it wasn't long before its users were talking to each other through their private accounts on the system, and so E-mail was invented. It was combined with other networks that were designed later and it grew into the Internet.

Aside from curiosity, people use the Internet for two reasons:

- **Keeping in touch** with others that have similar interests. With Internet, you can send E-mail through a local access point to its destination *via* various host computers. Note that a site "nearest" to you is actually one with the least number of hops, or hosts, in between, rather than being the least distance away. In some areas you can chat on-line, and in others you can send video and voice signals.

- **Getting information**, from the storehouses of knowledge that are part of the system. You would download files from where the experts in your chosen subject are.

The biggest problem with both is *finding* anything (or anyone)! There is no phone book, but there are one or two "WHOIS" databases you can access, relating to specific areas, in addition to third party books with listings, available from any book store. Under normal circumstances, you would know where your co-respondent is before you start, but if you know the site, you could at least send a message to *postmaster*, who may be able to help.

On the same basis, the most common way of finding where data is, is word of mouth, and you would have an account set up where you propose to get your files from, but you can get around this. Most times, once you contact the destination, you can use *anonymous* when prompted for a name, and your E-mail address as a password. This procedure is called *anonymous ftp*, since FTP (*File Transfer Protocol* – see below) is used for the downloading.

Accessing the Internet

You need a *service provider*, who will give you a link into the Internet. If you're a student, or part of an educational or government establishment, it's likely you have an account set up already (this was originally the only way you could get on). Otherwise, you can get text-only access to almost anywhere by issuing your commands through an on-line service, such as CIX, Compuserve or Delphi (or even FIDO connected Bulletin Boards). This is not full access, though, and can be difficult, particularly when trying to find people.

There are also *Public Access Sites* (like *Demon*), and you can set up a gateway/router running your own version of:

- UUCP, or Unix to Unix Copy Protocol, which is not restricted to Unix. It's modem-based, and is good for E-mail and *Usenet* access.

- TCP/IP, the standard access method, available from many shareware and commercial sources, and due to be included in later versions of Windows (see Chapter 20).

DOS/Unix experience is handy, because almost all of the Internet uses a Command Line Interface (CLI). In other words, no pictures! You only need to know how to get around directories, though.

Conversation

One of the "Internets" making up the Net is *Usenet*, which is a system of distributed Bulletin Boards looking after discussion groups, or chatlines (thousands of them), who regularly gather, so to speak, to exchange views and comments. All members in a group will either share hard disk space set aside for them, or receive a regular newsletter based on the member list (a *mailing list*).

Usenet Groups

There are eight main categories of these:

alt	alternative newsgroups; humour, controversy, etc.
comp	computer related.
news	announcements.
rec	recreational/hobbies.
sci	scientific.
soc	sociology.
talk	chatter and general debate.
mis	anything else.

Each is subdivided into its own specialist areas. You need *newsreader software* in order to participate.

(N)Etiquette

The Internet was originally used by professionals, or at least those who used it with serious intent. That doesn't mean to say they aren't helpful and courteous but, while ignorance can be understood, stupidity isn't (often). The point is that as they all came from similar establishments, and more often than not used Unix, they all thought and behaved in the same way, and life was in some way predictable. Indeed, you couldn't get on the Internet unless you were vouched for by somebody else.

As a result, many long-term users regard the net as their territory and can actually get quite grumpy with people who appear not to know what they are doing, although that says a lot more about them than it does about you!

Common courtesy and common sense prevail, as it does with Bulletin Boards (see Chapter 11). If you join a factual discussion group, don't express opinions, and *vice versa*. Others may be more easy going, or even seem to be run by anarchists – there are rumours of users who are a PITA (see *Glossary*) being sent virus-filled files as a lesson! This is known as a *mail bomb*, and is actually more likely to be a *very* large file (a dictionary perhaps?) that will cost you a lot to download.

It helps other readers if, when you reply to a message, you include a bit from the one you are replying to (with a > at the beginning of each line), as many users delete messages as they go along to save disk space, and may not remember what you're talking about. Don't include all of the message, because it will just be something else to eat up disk space at the destination.

One 1K message sent to 10, 000 users takes up 10 Mb of disk space somewhere, and bandwidth to get there, which is paid for by somebody, if not you. The replies generated may well take up 5 times that, particularly if you've said something controversial and others send *flames* in return (flames are messages of an incendiary nature).

Replies to replies will take up more, and so it goes on, resulting in large crashes due to congestion in the order of tens of megabytes per hour. One very good reason why advertising is not allowed!

Any advertising that does occur, BTW, is known as *spam*, which is the term for junk E-mail on the Internet. Stuff that nobody wants, but costs you in downloading time, which neatly describes advertising.

Remember that, although you might pay a fee to a service provider, the Internet is provided free by other people; you therefore have no rights! As there is no "police force", you are your own moderator and need to exercise your own self-discipline.

Smileys

There are aids to getting your message across, where you can't wave your hands to aid your communication. They come directly from your keyboard, and are inserted into your messages to lift the tone a bit. They are collectively known as *smileys* (look at them sideways):

:-)	Happy face.
:-(	Sad face.
;-)	Winking face.
:-{)	Happy face with moustache.

Abbreviations are also used, for shorthand (BTW = By The Way, for instance), and they are listed in the Glossary.

USE CAPITAL LETTERS WHEN YOU WANT TO SHOUT, but that's often rude.

Addressing

The Internet can be used to send E-mail to several on-line services, such as CIX, Compuserve, America On-Line and many Fido-connected BBSs, each of which, unfortunately, has its own way of addressing. The standard is:

```
name@service.somewhere.domain
```

For example:

```
frednurk@cix.compulink.co.uk
```

Names go from left to right, from the specific to the general. Each part is separated by a delimiter, commonly a full stop (the @ is only there for humans, and means "at"). The *domain* is actually the country, for addresses outside the USA.

Getting To Internet

The following is how to get *to* the Internet from your service:

Fido

This is a system of interconnected Bulletin Boards. A Fido address looks like a first and last name, with a set of numbers, like fred nurk at 1:123/37.4. All you need do is put a full stop between the names and reverse the numbers:

fred.nurk@p4.f37.n123.z1.fidonet.org.

Compuserve:

At the Send prompt, type INTERNET:address, such as INTERNET:frednurk@cix.compulink.co.uk.

Coming From Internet

CIX:

CIX id@cix.compulink.co.uk

Compuserve:

Use Compuserve ID number(e.g.

XXXXXXX.XXXX@compuserve.com)

Use a full stop rather than a comma in the Compuserve ID.

You can't always make connections with every service; Prodigy is not available, for example, and you can't send from Compuserve to MCI Mail, although you can do it directly, without Internet's intervention.

File Transfer

The *File Transfer Protocol* (FTP) allows file transfer between computers over the Internet.

Binary files must be sent as text, because much equipment is pretty basic and can only cope with 7-bit ASCII. Conversion can be done with a UUencoder, with UUdecoding at the other end. Alternatively, *Multipurpose Internet Mail Extension* (MIME) can be used.

FTP gets the files from where they live, places them on your access point from where you use normal downloading procedures to get them to your machine. The catch, therefore is two downloading sessions and bigger phone bills.

Commands

Not all FTP commands are the same, but will be listed if you type 'help' or ? at the prompt. The following work on most systems:

get	Copy a file from the remote computer to yours.
mget	Gets multiple files; * and ? are supported.
ls/dir	List the files in the current directory.
cd	Change directory.
binary	Switch to binary mode (for transferring binary files).
ascii	Switch to ascii mode (default).
bye	Logoff

Anonymous FTP

This is a way of logging in with the user name "anonymous" or "ftp".

Files are usually archived to save space; the most common format is *tar* (tape archive), but you may see *shar* (shell archives) instead. Tar archives can be unpacked by running the **tar** command (you may want to do a **tar t** on the file to see what's in it first).

Files are often compressed as well. For Unix, the most common scheme is the compress program, indicated by a .Z suffix on the file name. Sometimes, Arc or Zoo are used, which are combined archival and compression formats.

These are the common Unix file types:

```
SUFFIX          FTP TYPE

.Z              bin      compress
.arc            bin      ARChive
.shar           ascii    SHell ARchive
.tar            bin      Tape ARchive
.uu             ascii    uuencode/uudecode
.zip            bin      Zip
.zoo            bin      Zoo
```

When transferring .Z files, leaving the .Z part off will ensure the file is automatically decompressed. This may work with others.

To get a list of all file compression/archiving methods and the programs to uncompress/unarchive (on the PC, Mac, Unix, VM/CMS, AtariST and Amiga systems), FTP to the following sites and retrieve the listed file:

```
ftp.cso.uiuc.edu   /doc/pcnet/compression
gator.netcom.com   /pub/profile/compression.z
nic.switch.ch      /mirror/ftp-list/compression.z
```

The simplest way to initiate FTP would be to give the command:

```
ftp system-name
```

The *system-name* is the remote system you are connecting to. After a short wait, you will be prompted for your username. Taking the first example above:

```
FTP ftp.cso.uiuc.edu
```

If you don't have an account, some systems allow you to use *anonymous*, after which you are prompted for a password (or your real identity as the password).

Other systems use *guest*, or similar. If you have problems, try using a dash (-) as the first character of your password; this will turn off continuation messages that may confuse your ftp client.

After that, you should receive the FTP prompt:

```
ftp>
```

The interesting items will be in a directory called **/PUB** (note the forward slash). To get to PUB, use CD/PUB, and you can use DIR when you get there.

Again, using the example above:

```
cd/doc/pcnet/compression
```

Before transferring non-text files, you need to type:

```
binary
```

although it doesn't hurt to transfer text files with the binary command in action. Next, type:

```
GET filename.ext
```

UNIX is not restricted to eight letter file names (actually upto 256), and file names can contain characters not allowed by DOS, so when retrieving a file you often have to rename it. They are also case sensitive, so if you want a README file, you must type it like that. Similarly, you may also find directories and files with a mixture of caps/normal, so check that you're entering the text correctly.

You will see binary transfer is going on by a row of symbols (e.g. #) growing across the screen (every # means 1K). When it's finished you will be back at the **ftp >** prompt. get more files if you want, or type:

```
QUIT
```

Now you have to get the files from your service provider on to your machine, so you'll have to refer to their instructions. Delete them afterwards as a matter of courtesy to save their disk space.

Telnet

This is used for logging in remotely, or to another computer that you can control from your keyboard, assuming they give you permission! More specifically, it allows you to log on to another service from the one you are currently connected to, and use the new one as if you were connected to it directly, which is great if the one you eventually want is in Australia, since you will be connected at the local rate to the first one. The catch is that you will have two service charging rates, and the remote one may be in a different time zone, at their peak rate.

You must know the name of the service you want to use, and be a member of it, but there may be a guest account.

You would type:

```
TELNET <host>        e.g. cix.compulink.co.uk
```

after which you would log on, give your password and get up to whatever they allow you to. Remember, you are not talking to your own BBS, so you'll have to abide by different rules.

Help

At some stage, you will need some assistance, which comes mostly in the shape of *Archie* or *Gopher*. They're not programs, but *services*. Archie keeps file listings from different ftp sites; you send E-mail to Archie and the list of sites containing what you want comes back in a day or so.

For example, on CIX, type:

```
ARCHIE <topic>
```

or whatever, at the **IP>** prompt (having typed GO INTERNET), and the results will be a list of FTP sites and file specifications, identifiable as ARCHIE.LIS (or similar) in the IP directory. Having found what you want, use FTP (File Transfer Protocol) to retrieve it. For help, type:

```
HELP ARCHIE
```

You can get a help file by sending mail, with the word "help" somewhere in the text, to *archie@site_name* (see overleaf):

```
archie.ans.net        (North America)
archie.sura.net       (North America)
archie.unl.edu        (North America)
archie.funet.fi       (Finland/Europe Mai
archie.au             (Australia/NZ)
archie.doc.ic.ac.uk   (GB/Ireland)
archie.ncu.edu.tw     (Taiwan)
```

For example, use:

```
TELNET archie.doc.lc.ac.uk
```

When prompted, use *archie* as your login name (no password), then issue the filename. Once you get a hit, use FTP to get the file.

World Wide Web

Otherwise known as WWW or W3, this is an attempt to organise the information on Internet. It's a hypertext-based information tool that helps you use the web of stored information. Mosaic, for instance, is a browser program that runs under Windows or Unix to help you use WWW.

Gopher

Text-based forerunner of W3. An application that helps you navigate through resources using a simple menu structure. In this respect, it acts a bit like an off-line reader.

Most service providers have a *gopher client* you can use but, if not, you need to connect to a public gopher (use TELNET < gopher site >). Use *gopher* when asked to log in.

13

Fax

Technically, *Facsimile Transmission* (to give fax its full name) is the electronic transfer of a copy of a document from one point to another over some sort of transmission link, cable or otherwise (to you and me, it's just like using a long-range photocopier over the telephone, except that the quality is not so good). The original document is scanned and the different light and dark patches are converted into electrical signals that are transmitted.

It can therefore transmit complete pages of information (including pictures) through the telephone system as a series of scan lines arriving in exactly the same form as they were sent.

As to whether it's cost-effective or not depends on what you send; it can be extremely cheap if you need to send a couple of pages round the world quickly — certainly better than a courier. However, sending a 400 page book would take anything up to 3.5 hours — not a good idea at current prices!

A normal fax is a scanner which lays out the page into small areas (between .005 and .01") and notes where it detects dark patches (or not). This information is converted into what is called *modified Huffman code* and passed as a stream of on/off signals to an internal high speed auto-dial, auto-answer modem which sends the results down the telephone line. Everything is then reversed at the receiving end and date stamped, together with the identifying telephone numbers, which may give it some business credibility in opposition to Telex (some Government Departments accept faxed forms, but not necessarily signatures on them).

As it needs to make incoming data presentable, a fax machine will also contain a printer, unfortunately one that produces rather cheap-looking photostatic results, which sometimes requires special paper. A *plain paper fax* has output similar to a laser or inkjet printer.

The whole story started off around 1863, when the first fax transmission took place over the telegraph between Paris and Le Havre. It was invented by a Catholic priest camed Caselli.

The main problem was that the telephone hadn't been invented, so fax development had to wait before things could really get going! Even when things did get serious, there was a total absence of standards, which meant that transmission was safe only between identical machines.

As usual, though, somebody somewhere (in this case the ITU-T) has laid something down:

Group 1   Roughly equivalent to a 300 baud modem. Obsolete.

Group 2   Twice as fast, but still out of date. The standard of resolution on both meant that anything smaller than 6 point type was illegible. Being analogue systems, they were able to show the results in varying shades of grey (imagine them as slow scan TV).

Group 3   A standard for digital communications created in 1983 for machines that uses data compression techniques and transmits at 9600 bits per second, which means that a full A4 page can be sent in 30 seconds. Group 3 offers a choice of two resolutions as well, but using the higher one doubles transmission time. As group 3 operates on digital signals, marks on the paper are treated as black or white only.

Group 4   Designed for ISDN lines; you can send eight A4 pages per minute at 400 dpi with 64 shades of grey.

Class 1   For fax/modems. An extension to the Hayes command set that defines how fax software will control a modem; the bulk of the work is done by the software. Works sometimes.

Class 2   As above, but the bulk of the work is done by the fax. It is more complex and therefore less reliable. Sometimes works.

Like modems, faxes have extra facilities you may find useful. Some machines carry a spare RS232 socket so it can be used as a scanner.

There are memory stores for numbers, timed retries (for engaged signals), pretimed sending, group sending, speed changes according to line quality, identification of sender and receiver stamped on the copy, transaction reports, self checking at predetermined intervals, talk mode, repeat printing, error correction, page reduction and expansion...... As you can see, the list is endless.

However, not all fax machines are those you see around the office; there are other users with far higher standards to maintain, and for whom cost is less of an object. The machines they use don't come under the standard recommendations and are not often heard of at all. Some are used on news services, where the received document actually becomes the print master; similar machines are also used for fingerprints, but these are outside the scope of this book.

Fax (/Modem) Cards

These are expansion cards that take up a slot inside the computer; most modems now have fax capability built in, and these are no exception. They are useful, in that you don't have to print something, fax it, then throw it away. A document can be sent directly from your screen, as if it were being printed (to the computer, a fax card looks like a printer).

One reason for using a fax/modem card is that the end results are better, because one (or two) of the scanning stages are bypassed.

Tip: If you need to scan something, fax it to yourself from a normal fax machine.

You may need *Optical Character Recognition* software, because all fax files are sent in a graphic format and they will be needed in ASCII if you actually want to work on them. Legal documentation does need 100% accuracy, though, so be careful that your OCR software is good enough. However, Windows for Workgroups 3.11 can send fax files as text, which saves a bit of work, but only if both machines are using the same system.

Tip: If you have two V.17 (14,400) Class 1 fax/modem cards talking to each other, you can carry out *Binary File Transfer* (BFT), so you don't need OCR at the other end.

You need a reasonably powerful PC, in terms of the amount of memory and disk space that may be required – one A4 page at only 200 dots per inch resolution still requires half a megabyte of memory.

Using a fax

There are certain procedures when using fax of whatever type that help the system along for everybody. A fax machine will just churn the paper out as it arrives, and typically it's left unattended in the office corner, so the first person in the office gets the job of sorting out who gets what.

One trick that will help you get your paperwork where you want it is to attach a *cover sheet*. At its simplest, it could just be a short message saying who it's from and who it's bound for but, more importantly, it will contain the number of sheets sent. The time and date of transmission is not so important as the machine will probably take care of this anyway.

Not only is this a standard business practice, but it's a small courtesy for the person who has to sort the whole lot out while they're trying to make the coffee as well.

Alternatives

Try one of the commercial E-Mail systems which will undertake to send your uploaded files to any fax machine you care to nominate.

Summary

Although fax has overtaken telex as a means of exchanging documents between companies, there do remain one or two disadvantages.

The main one is authenticity. A normal fax machine stamps the time and date of transmission and the sending and receiving telephone numbers on each sheet that goes through. A fax card may not provide that sort of credibility, since anyone with a copy of a certain set of disk utilities could easily interfere with the data.

Minor niggles include using of special paper on some machines, the printing on which will fade away after a relatively short time.

One area where fax cards fall short of the standard equipment is in ease of use, where you would normally expect just to turn the machine on, dial a number and shove the paper into a slot when prompted. With a fax card, you need at least to know how to boot up a computer and work your way round the hard disk. For short jobs, where you have to wind the machine up specially, this could be quite time-consuming. Thus, not only could you end up spending lots more money, you could also take four times as long to do what you could with a dedicated machine!

Also, to receive incoming faxes unattended, you have to leave the computer and everything else switched on. In the same way that a microwave, while close, is not a replacement for a real oven, a converted computer is no replacement for a real fax. Unless you have good reasons for doing things otherwise, a PC Fax card should really be regarded as a complement to a dedicated machine.

Fax On Demand (Fax Back)

This is where voice boards, modems and software work in combination to provide a fax information service to callers. The voice board answers the call and guides callers into pushing buttons on a touch tone phone to get the documents they need. The documents themselves may come back straightaway, after pressing the **< Start >** key, or some time later on a separate call.

NOTES

Satellites

A communications satellite is a large solar-powered repeater in space which uses microwaves to get messages to and from it — an incoming signal is regenerated and retransmitted by repeater units, which are called *transponders* (as many as 46 is not uncommon). Separate frequencies are assigned for transmission to the satellite (the *uplink*) and from it (the *downlink*). As all terminals are listening to the downlink, correct reception at the original transmitter indicates correct reception, so a formal receipt/acknowledgement procedure is not required.

Some advantages of using satellites are that the Council can't cut the link with a JCB, weather affects transmissions very little and they are line of sight.

On the other hand, it's a lot of money up front to get the thing up there in the first place, it's risky and the distances involved mean delays throughout the whole process.

The distances are in fact about 22,000 miles, where the satellite is said to be in *geostationary orbit*; that is, it stays in the same location over the Earth.

Because of this height and the spread of the signals, the coverage area of one satellite (known as the *footprint*) can be as large as Africa, and as one satellite can be in contact with two or more earth stations at the same time (because of the line-of-sight coverage it enjoys), two continents can be put in touch with each other very easily.

However, the height also means that an average station to station path over the Earth could well be 60,000 miles, which will take about 1.2 seconds for a message to get through. This is not so much of a problem when the transmission is one way only, but a two-way conversation with delays can cause problems.

Where computers are concerned, a seeming one-way transmission is actually two-way, because of error checking and acknowledgement of message receipts, etc. Using all this with satellites could increase the total time on the system by as much as 80 percent.

Sometimes the operating software is modified to take account of the delays, but they can be better handled by a using a higher quality system, which in turn will allow larger block sizes to be sent which will mean fewer retransmissions.

Or you could send the data without waiting for acknowledgements and ensure that the blocks contain a code to identify the larger block to which they refer. Any offending blocks could be found and retransmitted later. This type of activity is called a *sliding window* response, where an acknowledgement may come after several blocks have been sent, coming back through another window in the transmission process.

15

Networking

Modern management needs information as fast as it can get it, and computers are used to make it readily available.

However, once a company gets its first computer, it isn't long before you get queues of people wanting to use it. The next step, of course, is to get one for each person in the queue.

Then, to stop people wasting time by walking between offices to exchange floppy disks, and to save money by making them all share one printer or accounts program, it's not long before all the computers are joined together and some lucky person finds themselves in charge of a network.

This is a common scenario, and many businesses grow to need computer systems capable of accepting and processing information from several users at the same time – a typical example is an accounts system which is fed with data from several operators at different terminals all day.

A network can also provide convenience. Companies with their headquarters in one city could connect with offices in another and print reports several hundred miles away.

In the future, when office equipment gets more intelligence built in, a report could be prepared and sent directly to a photocopier, where it could be printed, sorted and stapled in a fraction of the time it takes at present.

Indeed, it isn't that far away now. Laser printers already have the intelligence; all they need is the advanced sorting and stapling equipment that photocopiers already have ....

A Case In Point

A particular company had a minicomputer (the sort that occupied an air-conditioned room), inside which was all the details of the stock available; 20,000 items and increasing daily. When a manager wanted details of what was sold in a particular period in a particular area (a typical database query, in other words), he would have to create a report on a user-hostile terminal and request a printout, which would be delivered on a trolley in due course (does this sound familiar?).

The software on the minicomputer was sophisticated, but not enough for exactly what was wanted, so the relevant information was *retyped* into a spreadsheet on a PC so it could be manipulated and printed in a readable fashion on a laser printer. Depending on the amount of information required, and how much on the printouts was actually relevant, this process could take up to two days (and more), which was rather a lot in management time which could have been better spent making business decisions, or whatever managers do.

Then it was decided to connect the PC to the minicomputer directly, so that its data handling facilities were allied to the PCs processing power, and the report was diverted from the printer to the hard disk on the PC over the cable joining the two. Special software was then used to automate the extracting of information that was previously typed in, and the results imported into the spreadsheet. Total time; less than 5 minutes!

The expense of the equipment for networking was recouped in less than three weeks, and this is by no means an isolated example.

What Is A Network?

A network is a collection of computers able to communicate with each other, usually over a cable, but it can be radio or infra-red based. The original idea was to share expensive equipment; for example, instead of having a printer on every desk, idle most of the time, there could be one in the centre of the office used by everyone.

It's but a short step from sharing equipment to sharing information as well, like the company accounts, or employee names and addresses, and the network has evolved into a powerful tool for the management of a company's information, sometimes closely integrated with a database.

The most distinguishing characteristic is that data can enter or leave at any point and be processed at any workstation – any printer, for instance, can be controlled from any wordprocessor at any computer on the network.

History

Data networks have only existed for a relatively short time. Like most things in modern life, the pace of growth has only really accelerated in the latest eighth or so of the total time of development, being more than double in that short time than any in the previous time put together.

Although experiments had taken place previously, the world's first viable network, the ARPANet, wasn't built until 1970. This is because all previous attempts had been made with mainframe computers, which are even now outside the scope of most people. Although smaller computers had nowhere near the processing power of mainframes, somebody discovered that they could cheat slightly and get the same effect if they linked their PCs with the mainframe and used its facilities; getting in on its back, as it were. They didn't have to cart their machine to the same room, either – in fact, they didn't even need to be in the same building.

Not only was it a network, the ARPANET (it was named after Project ARPA) also introduced the concept of packet switching, which we've already come across.

It started off linking 4 sites, but within a year had covered 15 locations and 25 computers – in the late 1970s the total had grown to 64, to become the beginnings of the Internet.

Networks in General

If the network is to do with a single location (usually a building, or one or two floors in one), it is known as a *Local Area Network*, or LAN.

A *Wide Area Network*, or WAN, on the other hand, can spread over city or international boundaries, and is usually identified by having a third party (i.e. a telephone company) involved in making it work. As some internal systems (like in a university) can cover several miles without anyone else's assistance, distance alone is no indication of whether a network is Local or Wide Area.

Somewhere in between is a *Metropolitan Area Network* (MAN), which operates over the area of a city, or within a 50km boundary, with fibreoptics at 100 Mbps. Nodes are connected over 2 km distances.

Servers

Some computers in a network can be dedicated to a particular task. These are called *Servers*, because they *serve* their local communities in a particular way. The most common is a *file server*, which looks after data files and generally behaves like a giant disk drive.

The fileserver is often thought of as a controlling computer of a network, and referred to as just "The Server", but this is dependent on the type of setup. In a *peer-to-peer network*, each workstation has more or less equal status and handles some of the network chores, such as allowing a printer to be shared, so they can all be "servers" to some extent if required.

On the one hand, this allows great flexibility but, on the other, it can slow response times and increase management problems, especially when files and printers are spread out all over the place. A peer-to-peer network is otherwise known as a *distributed network*, as opposed to a *centralised, or server-based* network.

You may also find a *communications server*, which is simply a workstation containing modems to take the comms workload. Similarly, a *print server* will be a workstation that handles printing on behalf of the network. Neither machine needs to be powerful, just dedicated. In smaller systems, the file server often handles printing and communications all by itself.

One characteristic of peer-to-peer networks is that peripherals attached to workstations can be used by any other. In a server-based network, this is not the case without special software at each one. In those cases, all peripherals are attached to a server of some kind, to which all data bound for them is sent.

By the way, the term *workstation* in a network context should not be confused with the high performance standalone workstations marketed by some companies such as Sun or Apollo; i.e. those having high speed processors with massive RAM and storage facilities. In our context, it just means a computer on a network at which you work.

Sometimes a workstation will be known as a *client*, meaning its position relative to a server, as in *Client/Server relationship*. This has a special meaning relating to databases, which is in the Glossary.

Another phrase you will see is *Workgroup Computing*. It describes a group of people who wish to communicate with each other all the time, but only occasionally outside that group. Much software is written to increase workgroup productivity.

Software

Provided only one person is using it, anything normally used on a PC will run happily on a network, because the network operating system is supposed to provide an environment that allows it to. All you need to do is tell the program where to find the files it needs, which will not necessarily be on the computer it is run on.

The problems arise when the same *data files* need to be shared, and making sure that while somebody is using part of a file, the remainder is still accessible by others, or that any alterations are not lost. DOS does not normally allow this, so most programs expect to have the computer to themselves, and act accordingly.

Network-aware software, on the other hand, is specially designed to behave itself in the following ways:

- You can load several copies at once without it getting confused over such things as who's got colour screens, or not.

- It can recognise more disk drives from where it can get its data.

- It allows more than one person to share data files (i.e. it allows *file* or *record locking*), and lets them keep separate directories for their own use.

- It will understand that printers need to be released immediately after a print job. As it doesn't expect anyone else to be there, single user software will tend to keep hold of the printer until it is terminated.

Licensing

You can either buy a separate copy of a program for every person using it on the network, or use a *licence extension*, where a single copy of a product is licensed to a number of network users.

The Alternatives

Having decided that Networking may be an answer for you, it may be worth looking at the alternatives before we proceed.

Switching Boxes

If all you need is some kind of connectivity for a simple application (such as sharing a printer), why not just use a simple switching box?

The computers have cables going to the box, as do the printers; the switches, which can be electrical or mechanical, are used to route the data between them. The mech-

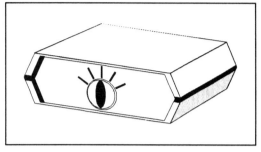

anical type consists of a switch that has to be turned to the right position before you print, whereas the electrical sort has some intelligence, in that it scans the lines for data and routes it accordingly. Note that you need a special switch box for Windows (just ask for one that is Windows-capable).

Multi-user Systems

These typically consist of a central computer controlling *terminal screens*, which are connected to it by serial cable, and which can do no work by themselves.

A terminal's job is to send information to the processor via the keyboard, and display information from it on the screen. A portion of the central memory is allocated to each terminal, as is processor time. Only *screen and keyboard information* is sent over the cabling.

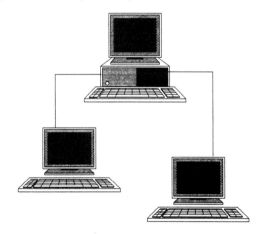

There are several types of multiuser system, based on mainframes to PCs, with operating systems to match, such as VAX or Xenix, which are highly specialised and way ahead of the PC with respect to data handling, but with a shortage of readily available application software (most of it has to be custom written). Because such a lot of software has already been written for DOS, it's worth looking at one operating system that may be useful.

Multiuser DOS

Multiuser DOS is a DOS-compatible, multi-user, multi-tasking operating system designed by Digital Research for use on 386SX, 386 or 486-based PCs, in conjunction with terminals for additional users. *Multi-user* means that several people can use the system at the same time; *multi-tasking* means that they can do so with several applications at once. The product is now owned by Novell and administered on their behalf by the *Master VARs* listed below:

- **Intelligent Micro Software Ltd**
  3 Archipelago Business Park
  Lyon Way
  Frimley
  Surrey GU16 5ER

  (0276) 686569

- **Concurrent Controls, Inc (CCI)**
  880 Dubuque Ave
  South San Francisco
  CA 94080 USA

  (415) 873 6240

- **Logan Industries**
  604 Mango Drive
  Melbourne Beach
  Florida 32951 USA

  (407) 984 1627

It is intended for small businesses and departments that already have a lot of DOS software and don't wish to spend more money on anything else.

DOS Sessions

Multiuser DOS can run more than one program at once – each runs in its own *DOS Session*, which is one of eight "pretend PCs" set up inside the host computer. The screen and keyboard are shared between DOS Sessions by using keyboard hotkeys, so that you move around your applications rather in the same way that you change channels on your TV set.

This has several benefits, especially if you regularly use two or three programs in the course of your working day; you don't continually have to leave one to start another and waste time as a result.

You can run up to eight DOS Sessions at once on any screen, so if you've got nine terminals, you can run 80 DOS Sessions, and thus 80 programs, provided the host computer is powerful enough. Each DOS Session can be rebooted with < Ctrl > < Alt > < Del > individually, so that other applications are not affected.

DOS compatibility

DOS applications and procedures are fully supported, as is Netware connectivity (16 connections at the same time), EMS (LIM 4) and DOS media, including CD-ROM drives, RAM disks or hard drive partitions up to 512 Mb. There is a special procedure for Windows.

Resource sharing

Each terminal can use all the facilities available on the host computer, including hard disks, printers, modems and the like (including network resources if connected to one). Printers can also be used on terminals.

Benefits of Networking

Although, at first sight, a multi-user system has much to recommend it, the real problems arise from software. Disk intensive processes, like accounting or databases, are ideally suited, but there would be trouble with DTP or CAD, for example, because terminals cannot handle sophisticated graphics (they are connected by serial cable, which is unable to cope with that much information).

The real attraction of a multiuser system is to allow several people to work on large jobs, a prime example being a busy accounting department with too many transactions for one person to handle (assuming you have no graphics requirement). It can also be simpler, and less costly to install and extend than a network.

However, networks can do anything a multi-user system can, and are better at processor and screen intensive tasks, such as spreadsheets and graphics applications, which are run locally (*at the workstation*). Typical advantages of installing a network include:

Distributed Processing	Programs are downloaded from a central point (i.e. the fileserver) and run *locally*. The network system does no processing, but merely provides storage space for data and programs. It's a false economy, therefore, to use underpowered workstations, because that's where people do their work.

Security   A workstation doesn't need disk drives, so you can:

- Stop people stealing your data and/or software.

- Keep viruses out.

Then again, terminals don't have disk drives, either.

Backing up   Where data is centralised, backing up procedures are more convenient and can be more closely controlled.

Shared resources   Equipment that would normally be sitting idle for long periods can be utilised more effectively when several people share the use of it.

Communication   Electronic mail around the office:

- Sending replies is easy, because the system remembers who sent the original message and sorts it out for you.

- Files can be attached to messages — saves paper!

- Appointments and schedules can be arranged between groups of people, so you can use the system like an alarm clock (resources, such as classrooms or overhead projectors, can be treated as people).

NOTES

16

Equipment Required

In an ideal world, a network should allow several different items of equipment to talk to each other and be mobile — wouldn't it be simple if you could just move things around with as much ease as you could move a coffee machine or a vacuum cleaner and still get them to work?

Unfortunately, life isn't like that! The varying hardware that a network needs to operate with is described in this chapter, while explanations of the types of network they refer to will be found in the next one.

Fileservers

Aside from the obvious, like the CPU matching the software (NetWare 386, for example, needs an IBM 386-based PC or compatible), you may need one with a casing very much larger than normal to accommodate the extra boards and hard disks you put in, although there is some consolation in that you won't need to pay up for much more than a mono monitor.

As servers are *I/O bound*, rather than *processor bound* (which simply means they handle much more in the way of input and output than actually calculating), the data bus should be carefully chosen. As workstations are connected to the file server, which is therefore the point through which the most traffic will travel, you may need to get something with a bit more muscle than the standard ISA bus, which could cause substantial bottlenecks. Better try EISA as a minimum, or VL-Bus or PCI when the technology matures. Having said that, light traffic loadings from a few users are well within the capabilities of the ISA bus.

Network operating systems don't normally need a maths coprocessor, so a 486SX is good enough, as is a 386/40 for most small networks. Just make sure you've got plenty of memory in it; although there's a theoretical minimum, you can never really have enough.

For example, Netware requires at least 2.5 Mb, plus a bit for the drive directories (they're kept in memory for speed), so you won't get away with less than 4 Mb; 8Mb if you've got 1 Gb of disk space.

A fileserver needs to be tough, because it will probably be running eight days a week. It also needs to be reliable since, if it doesn't work, its associated workgroup doesn't, either.

Many companies make fileservers specially with the above requirements in mind, with lots of RAM, space for expansion cards and multiple hard disks.

Hard disks

This particular item needs to be as reliable as possible, for obvious reasons; if it's in the file server, it's where the network data is stored, together with the complete operating system, and you would be well advised to have more than one, and not only for redundancy purposes; it will make things run faster as well.

Multiple disk drives can be *mirrored*, where two drives have identical data and each is updated at regular intervals. Both drives would be on one disk chain. With *Disk Duplexing*, on the other hand, data is written simultaneously to all disks. In this case, you can either have two drives hanging off one controller, or two complete drive chains.

As for running faster, all drives will be treated as one; that is, write requests will all happen in parallel, giving less of a bottleneck when many people want to use the hard disk; use multiple controllers for the same reason. However, the ability to do this is dependent on the network operating system. As far as performance goes, if you're forced to choose, you're better off spending money on a fast hard drive rather than a fast processor.

It's also worth mentioning that some manufacturers require this item to be formatted to their specifications, thus upsetting your own particular requirements, if you have them. Novell is one example, but see the *Software* chapter for good reasons why they do this.

Connectors, cables and terminators

Like drains, cables can account for a substantial part of installation costs without you seeing anything tangible for your money—but you still have to spend it, because they're often a major cause of failure. It's not uncommon for cabling to cost as much again as the networking equipment itself, although 20-30% is more realistic, and most of that is in installation costs rather than material. In view of that, the actual cost of cabling relative to the whole system could be as low as 5%, in which case it doesn't make sense to skimp.

There are hidden costs in using cable that is just not up to the job, in terms of reduced system performance and shorter cabling runs between machines, meaning that people will take longer to do their work and you will need extra hardware to boost signals, respectively. It may also affect your future expansion.

The trick with cabling is to install it after the telephone people have been in. If you're lucky, they will have used conduit with spare capacity, so you can place the network cabling inside it (coax benefits greatly from this).

Wiring problems, if you get them, are best solved with the help of both the building and electrical trades, because there are all sorts of strange regulations you may not know about. *Standard wiring plans* are available from all manufacturers, but they can be expensive. IBM's is used as a kind of shorthand; for example, Type 5 cable is two fibreoptic strands, whereas Type 8 is shielded twisted pair specially made to go under the carpet without showing up as a lump.

Cable needs management, too, if only to record where you lay it. The real reason, though, is to make sure it's the optimum length for maximum performance. A small network will only need a quick note on the back of an envelope, but you can progress to a database on a PC, or even a CAD system to produce your diagrams with.

The designation *10BaseX* (or whatever), where mentioned, decodes as follows:

```
10              Speed, as in 10 mbps
Base            Baseband
X               Max segment length/type; e.g.
                2=200'
                T=Twisted pair
                F=Fibreoptic
```

These are the types of cabling you may come across:

- **Thin Cable**, which is coax, for Ethernet, Token Ring or ARCNet. Each end of the cable has a BNC plug, which is connected to a T-piece, which in turn connects to the *Network Interface Card* (see overleaf).

- **Thick Cable**, for "normal" Ethernet. Heavy coax, yellow in colour. Often used as a backbone.

- **UTP/STP** *Unshielded Twisted Pair* for Ethernet or ARCNet (more rarely Token Ring). This is simply two insulated wires twisted around each other. STP, or *Shielded Twisted Pair*, has a metallic covering, making it more robust and less prone to interference. Both are terminated with American-style telephone connectors.

- **Fibre** This can be used on anything, but is expensive although it has a high bandwidth. It's major plus point is security, in that you can't tap it electromagnetically.

Network Interface Cards

Each workstation (and fileserver for that matter) will need a Network Interface Card (NIC) in order to operate on the network. This is an expansion card that the connecting cables are attached to, and will look somewhat like this:

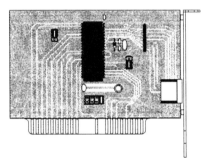

Network Interface Cards reduce the amount of cabling between computers (you would need a minimum of twelve), by converting data into packets for transmission in serial fashion along a single wire.

There are industry standard NICs as with anything else, and most are based on the Novell NE2000 or NE1000 (for Ethernet) and the IBM 16/4 (for Token Ring). Other companies, such as 3Com, or Intel, have products of equal status.

NICs need software to activate them. If they are compatible with the industry standards, the network operating system will use them automatically. If not, they will need their own.

For a full discussion of the ins and outs of installing NICs, see *Expansion Cards* in *Troubleshooting* (Chapter 24).

Remote Reset PROMs

There is a socket for one of these on every NIC. They are used in diskless workstations which would otherwise have no method of booting up. The PROM has enough intelligence to interrogate the server when the computer it's in is switched on, and download the operating system it needs (i.e. DOS) from there. On the server, you can have as many versions of DOS as there are workstations, all in separate directories, and all taking up disk space.

Remote Boot PROMs are specially made for each type of network operating system, and interface card. Theoretically, they are able to work in compatible cards as well, but it's not always the case.

Hubs

A hub is a box into which all the cables from the PCs on the network are inserted. Not every network needs one, but the trend is towards them because they can be more than just a concentrator. Hubs aid reliability, as when one machine goes down, it doesn't affect any others. Of course, if the hub goes......

Switching hubs allocate bandwidth on demand for hungry applications, such as voice- or video-annotated E-mail. As circuits are created only between workstations that require them, PCs not involved are not burdened, and the data transfer rate between the relevant stations is quicker.

Hubs can be *active* or *passive* (active ones have their own power supply). Their size can range from an expansion card in a PC, through a small box, to a large cabinet under the stairs in a large company.

As an active hub amplifies and regenerates signals, the cable runs between them can be longer. You can daisy chain hubs together to increase the range of the network, but not when connecting passive to passive.

Intelligent hubs can provide diagnostics, which can often be interrogated from a workstation with suitable software. At the very least, this will be in the form of LEDs on the front panel which tell you when data is flowing. Hubs may also be able to provide bridging and routing facilities (see Chapter 18, *Internetworking*).

NOTES

Types of Network Available

There are as many types of network as there are circumstances. Finding the most cost-effective to suit yours really depends on establishing your priorities — it's worth bearing in mind that the cheapest solution is not always the best. A cheap (as opposed to less expensive) solution often costs more in the long run, and not just in hardware.

Remember that the network itself isn't important — the information being circulated round it is, together with the increase in productivity resulting from its successful manipulation. Company survival may depend on rapid reaction to market changes, and the network's function is therefore concerned with ensuring that the right information is able to be accessed by the right person at the right time. What that means is that you should get a network to suit your circumstances rather than change the way you work because you got one cheap from down the road; for example, if security from eavesdropping is most important to you, then swallow hard and fork out for fibreoptics!

Topologies

Once upon a time, there were distinct ways of laying networks out; namely *The Star*, *The Ring* and *The Bus*, but the boundaries are becoming less obvious as time goes on.

In view of this, the above topologies will be explained within the descriptions of the common types of network that follow, each of which may use any one, or a mixture.

Zero-Slot Networks

Computers can be joined through their serial or parallel ports, which is a very cheap way to connect (less than $25 or £25 in some cases). A direct connection is mostly used for file transfer, typically between a desktop computer and a laptop, but you can form a network this way as well.

> How it works is quite simple. Each workstation loads a small program into memory which diverts all requests for equipment not on that workstation to the Server through the RS232 or parallel port. That is, the satellite PC is informed that it has extra drives and printers available to it, and that they can be accessed via the serial port. Thus, it's fooled into thinking that these items are actually installed.
>
> The server will have a similar program whose only function is to watch the serial port for such requests, which puts the two machines in touch and sends the information wanted on its way.
>
> LANs set up in this manner are often called 'zero-slot' LANs because none of the computer's internal expansion slots are taken up with interface cards.
>
> As performance is not of the best, this method is suitable mainly for shared access to a printer with occasional file transfer or systematic backing up, or for any situation where non-permanent networking requirements exist.

ARCNet

Short for *Attached Resources Computing*, this was one of the first commercially available LANs which uses *token passing* over coaxial cable to cater for heavy data loads (a "token" is an "electronic courier" to which stations that want to send can attach data). However, unlike *Token Ring* (see later), where a station can only transmit to the next station in line when it has the token, Arcnet stations can broadcast to all the others (approximately in the order of workstation ID numbers) at the same time, using a star or bus topology. The star is shown below:

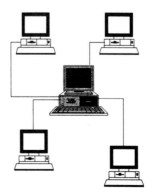

ARCNet is a switched network that needs a hub with which to operate. Switching ensures that only those stations that need to talk to each other are actually connected at any time.

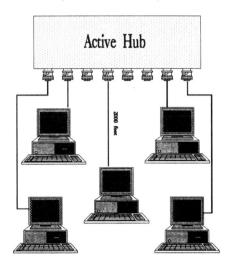

Whereas Token Ring and Ethernet interface cards have a unique address number burned into them at the time of manufacture (make sure cloned ones don't all have the same one!), ARCNet station IDs are set with switches on the card, and must be between 1 and 255 (0 is reserved). The PC with the lowest number is "the controller", which ought to be the most powerful one to cope with the extra traffic.

Cabling

Coaxial cable (RG-62 or 59), but some companies have been able to adapt it for use it with UTP. Fibre is also available. RG-62 requires a 93 ohm terminator, and RG-59 a 75 ohm.

Limitations

The maximum number of workstations is 255.

The maximum span of the network is 20,000 feet, with 2,000 feet between a workstation and an active hub (reducing to 100 feet with a passive hub). The same figures apply between hubs.

It is not bridgeable, as ARCNet NICs don't have unique 48-bit IDs.

In Short

ARCNet's transmission speed is slow (2 Mbits per second, with 20 for ARCNet plus), but it's quite dependable. In fact, its efficiency and relative cheapness still gives it the occasional edge over more modern and faster systems.

Token Ring

In concept, a ring looks like this:

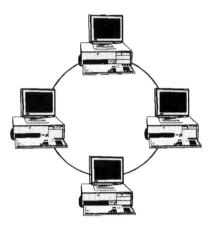

Messages go round continually in one direction until claimed by the workstation they are intended for, so collisions between messages don't occur, as they do with *Ethernet* (see below).

On *Token Ring*, as designed by IBM, the first station passes a token (or a "permission to send" message) to the next in line, which can either send data or pass the permission on, so only the station that has the token can gain access to the network. The permission is given for a preset period, and when the station has finished transmitting, or its time runs out, the token is forwarded anyway.

If one device becomes unserviceable, the network will fail unless there is a bypass facility, such as that offered by a *Multistation Access Unit*, in which case, it becomes more like:

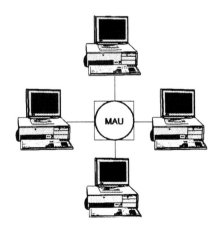

Which is really a *Star Ring* layout. The cable ring is still there, provided as circuitry within the MAU, where a relay is opened or closed as a connecting plug is inserted or extracted, or a Network Interface Card is activated (MAUs click from time to time as relays are activated; this is quite normal). Each station must connect to a Multistation Access Unit.

Enhanced MAUs can provide diagnostics which can be interrogated by network management software.

Cabling

Type 6 IBM cable is used, in set lengths; *adapter cables*, for example are 8 feet long, and used to connect workstations to MAUs. *Patch cables*, on the other hand, can be 8, 30, 75 or 150 feet long, and are used for extending adapter cables or connecting MAUs (from the *Ring Out* socket on one to the *Ring In* socket on the other).

Inside the cable, there will be a minimum of two wires terminating in either a 9-pin D-sub connector (at the NIC) or a proprietary IBM connector.

Coax used for Token Ring is RG59.

You can use UTP, but note that, while a 4 mbps system can accommodate up to 260 nodes using 100m each to get to the MAU, a 16 mbps system would struggle to cope with 70 nodes with only 80-85m each (the figures are actually dependent on a calculation involving distances, station count and type of cable, and each is variable as the others change). However, with only a few workstations on a 16 mbps system you could push this to 300 feet from a MAU. Poor signal quality is possible, though.

Limitations

For 4 mbps systems, the maximum number of nodes is 96, and MAUs 12. The maximum length between MAUs is 300m.

In Short

Token Ring is costly to install (especially the 16 mbps version), but is often better able to cope with heavy workloads than Ethernet, due to its "regulated" way of working (you could say it's more polite). Consider using it if you want a large network (plus of 2-300 users) capable of handling data in large amounts.

Because the circuitry is in a box and governed by relays, Token-Ring is often a good choice when the equipment will be installed for the use of non-computer literate people, or those who would not necessarily appreciate the implications of pulling a wire out of the back of their machine. It is more forgiving than Ethernet in this respect, where a bad connection will stop the system working.

A good use of Token Ring is where strict timing is important (such as in a car factory, where milling machines and suchlike have to make adjustments in times down to one-thousandth of a second or so), or when you want connectivity with IBM 3270-type mainframe computers, which are built round it.

Ethernet

Ethernet is a *broadcast system*, which was originally developed by Digital, Intel and Xerox. Stations on the network can send messages whenever they want, with no precedence or order. Although all stations may receive all the messages sent, only the correct one will respond. It's called Ethernet because it's not meant to be tied to any particular medium; you can use it with radio if you want (*Ether* was supposed to be a hazy word). It's typically used in a *bus configuration*, where each computer is attached to a long cable, which is terminated at each end with a small resistor (50 ohms) that eliminates any unwanted signals.

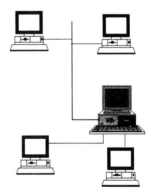

The *tree network* is a combination of buses, where sub-branches are hung off the main one and the workstations in turn are hung off those. It has all the advantages and disadvantages of a bus net, but although it seems as simple to set up, it can actually be quite complicated to implement. It also needs branch splitting hardware. A *cellular net* is more like a hexagonal bus (resembling a ring with terminals off).

Messages are split up into packets and sent round the system in short bursts separated by comparatively long idle periods, each having its address tacked on the front, and being reassembled at the receiving terminal. There's nothing smart about it; the packets are merely broadcast nearer and nearer to their destination until they hit.

Some errors (the wrong address, for example) mean that the message is totally ignored. In practice, there is a short delay before any error is detected so there must be a *minimum packet length*, otherwise transmission could finish before mistakes are found.

The cable works like a telephone party line, in that only one station can transmit at any time; all stations are allowed to transmit freely, but if a collision occurs between packets, the culprits back off for a short time and then retry.

The most commonly used system for this is *Carrier Sense Multiple Access* (CSMA), which comes with either Collision Avoidance (CA) or Collision Detection (CD) procedures – in practice, they are identical, since if you detect a collision, you simply avoid it.

Looked at it in more detail, the line is sensed for activity by the originating sender and is "acquired" if nothing is happening. Line voltage drops significantly if two stations transmit at the same time, and the first station to notice this sends a high voltage jamming signal around the net to signify a collision. The stations trying to transmit then back off for a random time interval, this being doubled if it happens again. If this happens more than 16 times an error condition is reported.

A humorous way of looking it is to imagine a hotel corridor with rooms on either side, where the occupants are trying to sneak into each others' bedrooms.

The first thing any of them do will be to check if the corridor is clear (line acquisition). If so, he will arrive at the door of his destination (interface) and say the correct password, being admitted if all is well.

If the journey along the corridor is disturbed by another bent on a similar errand, or the wrong door or password is used, then both will scurry back to their rooms and try later (retransmission).

Frames

The *frame structure* (or how the packet is constructed) is defined by IEEE standard 802.3, but 802.2 is also current (NetWare 3.12 defaults to it). Naturally, the workstation NIC must be told to use the same frame structure as the Server; with NetWare, this is done with a line in the NET.CFG file.

Ethernet II

Used by Unix or DECNet networks. The frame structure is different to 802.3, so the two cannot coexist on the same cable.

10baseT

A standard for Ethernet transmissions laid down in 1990, defining a baseband 10 Mbps signalling speed over twisted pair cabling through hubs, giving it a star topology.

The hub provides a distribution point which can be a simple junction box or something intelligent that can cope with routing, bridging, switching and other management functions, as well as multi-protocol support. It can often be controlled from the front panel.

10baseT hubs can send a signal (known as the *Link Beat Signal*) to check the integrity of the cables and devices attached. You just check the LED on the hub to see if all is well.

Ethernet can only have a certain number of hubs within a segment; 4, in fact. *Stackable hubs* can combine internal connections to simulate a larger device, so you don't use up the hub limit within a segment.

Fast Ethernet/100BaseT

"Fast Ethernet" is a generic term for a variety of systems running at 100 Mbps (Ethernet's standard speed is 10 Mbps). One is 100BaseVG-AnyLAN; "VG" stands for *Voice Grade*, referring to the quality of the cable.

The extra speed is achieved by dividing the time each packet is transmitted by 10, giving you ten times the packet speed, although this does reduce the cable length somewhat.

Switched Ethernet

This uses switching boxes that create dedicated circuits internally on the fly, so it only makes connections between nodes that actually need to talk to each other, thus making better use of currently available bandwidth.

Note that it will only boost performance in certain circumstances:

- Where utilisation is more than 35%.

- Your network is getting sluggish.

- There are no bottlenecks.

It is not cost-effective where your network has only one server and there is minimal traffic anyway; you would be better off increasing the Server's connectivity.

ISO Ethernet

This is essentially 2 networks running over one set of 10BaseT cabling. The second one, the ISO part, adds another 6 Mbps of bandwidth and sits on top of the normal Ethernet channel, being split into 64 Kbps segments which can be used by themselves or merged.

Cabling

For **Thin Ethernet**, RG 58 (10Base2) coaxial cabling rated at 50 Ohms. You would use a T-piece at the NIC and attach a cable to each side of it, making one long trunk, at both ends of which you would put a 50 ohm terminator on the unused part of the T-piece.

Thick Ethernet (10Base5) uses a thicker coax, yellow in colour. At the workstation, you need a *transceiver* with a *drop cable* to the PC, terminated with a 15-pin AUI, connector (looks like a game port). The transceiver's connection is screwed through the yellow cable.

UTP/STP (*Unshielded/Shielded Twisted Pair*) cable has the advantages of lower cost, less disruption if a workstation goes down (due to the hub) and longer cable runs. Many interface cards come with connections for UTP and coax.

10BaseT uses 2 pairs of wires; pins 1 and 2 for the first pair, and 3 and 6 for the second. Here are the pinouts:

Pin	Function	Colour
1	Transmit	White/orange
2	Transmit	Orange/White
3	Receive	White/Green
4		Blue/White
5		White/Blue
6	Receive	Green/White
7		White/Brown
8		Brown/White

You can join UTP/STP to coax by:

- Using a hub with an AUI adapter and attach a thin Ethernet transceiver to the AUI port.

- Getting a hub that can cope with both.

- Using a translator, into one end of which you plug coax and UTP in the other.

Limitations

185m per segment for Thin Ethernet, with 30 nodes on it. You can extend this with up to 4 repeaters, but each one will count as a node. The maximum length in this case would be 925m. You can get over the repeater count with a stackable hub.

Thick Ethernet can have 500m per segment, up to 2,500 with 4 repeaters (again, each is a node). Transceiver cable can be up to 50m.

In short

Ethernet, in particular the thin variety, is easier and cheaper to install than Token Ring, and is most cost-effective for up to around 200 users running common applications. Expect delays, though, if you've got 5 or 6 people loading Windows at the same time....

Although the connection can be removed from the NIC without affecting the rest of the system, the cable itself must not be broken, otherwise the network will not operate, as it will be unable to broadcast signals.

Because there's no guarantee that either errors will be detected or that a signal will get through within a particular time, this sort of system is better geared to an office rather than a factory, where real-time applications are less important.

FDDI

100 Mbps, based on timed Token Passing, using a ring or star-wired topology over fibreoptic or copper media. It's used mainly as a high speed backbone.

It can cope with up to 500 stations in a single ring up to 200 km in length.

Wireless LANs

These can be radio or   ra-red based. They are useful for staying connected while you move about (within   :, of course). You don't need to lay cables everywhere, either, so you can set up a network in a couple of hours (great for demos). They are slower and costlier than conventional networks, but make up for it in convenience.

ATM

Asynchronous Transfer Mode is intended to make better use of bandwidth. It does this by working more like a telephone system, where "permanent connections" are made only between nodes that need to transmit. In other words, a circuit is created by switching when it is required, and broken up into its constituent parts once the conversation has finished. It moves cells over *virtual circuits*, and is intended for use with fibreoptics.

ATM has a fixed packet size of 53 bytes; 5 are for the *header* used for routing, and the rest for the payload, which is ignored by the network. The packets are organised, so are more efficient. This allows ATM to handle video transmissions in particular, which need consistency.

Setting up connections across ATM is called *signalling*. It has two types of *virtual circuits, Permanent* and *Switched*, as with X.25.

Each node has its own link into a central "exchange", which makes and breaks the appropriate connections. You can set up several *Switched Virtual Circuits* (SVCs) from a single node, and they can last for a single cell, a multi-cell packet or a complete network session.

ATM has the potential for seamless integration of various systems, including computer networks, with at least 150 Mbps bandwidth available. In theory, you could knit the whole of the country into one giant network, with similar response times wherever you are.

NOTES

18

Internetworking

Companies often want to join networks in different cities and make them look as one to the average user. "Internetworking" is the connection of two or more Local Area Network, with the aim of turning them into one transparent entity, possibly a Wide Area Networks, which will mean involving telephones.

A simple connection to another LAN can vastly increase the effective range of the original; for example, where a Token-Ring network is limited to 96 nodes, just join it to another to get 192. This could be done in a building with different LANs on different floors.

Alternatively, you may be wanting to upgrade your present equipment and are unwilling to actually part with it; joining the old and new together would be a good solution.

You could also require to access the company network with a portable computer (see below), or from home, as you would when teleworking. In this situation, your computer could be either:

- **A workstation in its own right**, in which case programs and data are sent over the telephone line. More powerful equipment is needed for this, if not an ISDN line, as a telephone connection only runs at 1% of the speed. I wouldn't like to try loading Windows!

- **A terminal off a workstation** on the network, in which case, only screen and keyboard data are transmitted either way, so you can get away with more modest equipment.

Portables

The simplest connection is either a serial or parallel cable joined directly to another computer, commonly used for data transfer, but it's quite common for portables to be used directly as workstations.

As very few portables have expansion slots, this generally means using an Ethernet adapter that attaches to the parallel port, or using software that allows the portable to attach to a workstation and connect through there (*Lap2Lan* springs to mind).

Otherwise, you could use a *docking station* which is permanently attached to the network, into which you plug your portable. The nearest equivalent to that is a *port replicator*. It could be, of course, that your portable has connectivity built in, but this is comparitively rare, especially now that PCMCIA exists, but it doesn't always work. You need software drivers for each card, for one thing and, for another, the standards are not always adhered to. On top of that, the cards and connectors are quite flimsy and not up to being constantly connected and disconnected.

Networks

As far as complete networks go, however, there are several ways of connecting different ones, and the equipment used to do this is described below. Unfortunately, the product descriptions don't always match up to their names, so you will have to do the appropriate reading between the lines for the hybrids.

Generally, though, there are four types of equipment; the *repeater*, the *bridge*, the *router* and the *gateway*, some of which can use either Dial-up, Kilostream, Megastream, X.25 or ISDN connections to remote sites if required.

Try not to think of them just as "little black boxes", as a PC is often used to do the job, with suitable expansion cards inside. Not only that, intelligent hubs often have bridging and routing facilites built in.

The Repeater

The repeater's function is to compensate for attenuation and to support longer distance cabling by regenerating signals. Everything a repeater hears on one LAN is repeated on another, with the singular disadvantage that traffic is doubled on either side of it. The networks concerned need to be of the same type (e.g. Token Ring to Token Ring), although the software running them can differ, as repeaters work on the electrical signals themselves rather than on the information contained in them.

The Bridge

Bridges can be used for extension purposes, like repeaters, but are better used for joining networks that need to use another's resources, or for segmenting the cabling system and allowing more than one message to exist at a time, thus making better use of the bandwidth and reducing intersegment traffic.

It does this by reading the address of every frame it comes across and deciding which ones will pass to the other segment. In other words, it acts like a sentry.

As bridges don't understand packets, they are protocol independent, but the main thing is to ensure that they use the same *addressing scheme* (such as the IEEE 802 series; 802.3 for Ethernet or 802.5 for Token-Ring). This is not like using the same protocol, but making sure that everyone uses postcodes. Otherwise, it doesn't matter what protocols or software are used – it is entirely possible to run Novell's IPX, 3Com's XNS, DECNet and TCP/IP across a bridge all at the same time. Remember, all the bridge does is pass packets on to their destinations.

An *internal bridge* lives inside a file server as a second interface card. An *external bridge* could be a workstation. To make one, take an old PC (floppy-only will do), put 2 network interface cards in it and run bridging software, having connected each card in the PC to a LAN.

When they connect two LANs directly, internal and external bridges are known as *local*. Where something like a telephone or satellite link is used between them, they become *remote*.

Local bridging is a cheaper option than the remote kind, because modems aren't needed. It is not recommended that remote bridging is done internally, i.e. from a fileserver, due to the performance degradation you might get.

Aside from being remote or local, bridges can come in enhanced versions; some LANs have more than one bridging connection between them, which can give a circular feel to the system. In this case, it is possible for a non-intelligent bridge just to circulate information around endlessly, which stops other stations sending because the cables are full. *Spanning tree bridges* are able to detect and break such circles by turning off certain links, which can be restored later if any of the other links becomes inoperative.

However, this does mean that the capacity of the inoperative links is wasted, so a *load balancing bridge* will also allow two or more ports of a bridge to send data to the same destination, thus sharing the data between the ports and combining their capacity.

A *learning bridge* can store the addresses of the stations that identify themselves on the net, saving you the bother of setting them all up manually.

A *source routing bridge* can make limited routing decisions based on special data placed in a packet by its originator.

Bridges can introduce delays, since the whole packet is stored before the decision is made to send it on. As they still forward all packets destined for every workstation, you could get what is called a "broadcast storm".

Routers

Although some bridges can direct data packets based on their address, it is still a bit of a hit-and-miss affair, because it's more often than not a "forward or discard" decision, which deals only with networks to which the bridge is directly attached, so traffic can be reduced, but not by much within a segment where traffic is allowed. Thus a packet is sent towards its destination down narrower and narrower channels until it finally arrives.

A router, on the other hand, can take account of addressing information in the packet, and even forward data to networks not directly attached to its own, due to on-board processors that can deduce where addresses are, and maybe use the telephone to get to them. It therefore provides *alternate path selection*, with the ability to route traffic the most efficient way, giving a level of fault tolerance as well as reducing excess traffic. Because it makes such decisions, a router operates one layer higher than a bridge in the ISO model.

Routers transfer packets between networks of dissimilar topology, and are protocol dependent; where bridges don't normally modify a packet, routers can extract the data from one type (e.g. Token Ring), insert it into another (X.25) and ensure it's placed into something else at the destination.

A router can get quite busy, what with constantly broadcasting its own status, updating that of others, checking addresses, making routing decisions, and the like, so routers are slower than bridges, which means you get most performance when you keep traffic local.

Brouters

Brouters exist midway between bridges and routers. They can route one or more protocols and bridge all others. They are slower than bridges, but smarter.

Gateways

Gateways typically connect networks to different equipment, such as mainframes or minicomputers that don't even share the same routing protocol (e.g. NetWare to TCP/IP) or maybe have different architectures. Typically, they could be used from a LAN to an X.400 or other external service (e.g. PC-mainframe links – see below).

As with a bridge, the gateway needs at least two interface boards in a workstation; one for the LAN and another for the host system connection, which may be through a modem and telephone link (if remote) or a coaxial cable, if direct. The gateway will emulate the software required at both ends, thus acting as an interpreter.

Software used with a gateway will need to provide some sort of terminal emulation facility, so that the workstation will behave as a terminal of the host (PCs tend to use ASCII, for instance, where hosts may use something like EBCDIC, IBM's version of the same thing. Keystroke coding will also be different).

What to choose?

If all you want is simply to extend your network, choose a repeater (but remember that repeaters don't provide isolation, which is useful when troubleshooting). Just make sure that your LAN is lightly loaded. Some repeaters, by the way, can convert between media; that is, coax Ethernet to UTP.

Bridges do the same job, but support multiple protocols on like systems, such as a group of Ethernets or a group of Token Rings. Use a bridge to link heavily loaded LANs, and make more bandwidth available, by providing segmentation inside a single site.

Routers are more complex, thus slower, but can connect LANs to the outside world. Like bridges, they can ensure that only data packets that need to be in a particular location are actually there.

Use a gateway where the routing protocols are different (PC to mainframe links). However, if only one PC on the network needs access, try using terminal emulation software – it's cheaper.

There is nothing to stop you using many combinations of the above in the same network, or even in the same node, in a comms server.

PC-Mainframe Links

There are two ways a PC can integrate with larger computers:

- **Terminal Emulation,** or making the PC behave like one of the mainframe's usual terminals (say, a VT-100 for a DEC). Although only screen and keyboard information is sent to a terminal, file transfer could be available as well, typically using Kermit or XModem.

- **Full synchronous links,** with the PC and host processing in sympathy over a network, such as Token Ring (IBM) or Ethernet (DEC).

Any DEC Vax using VMS can act as a server for a PC network. Others with Unix would use TCP/IP, and NT would also be available.

Note that most mainframes only support 7-bit ASCII, so can only cope with printable characters (ASCII 32-127).

19

Performance And Security

How good a network is depends on the amount of traffic carried, and the capabilities of the equipment on it. For example, performance can be limited by the network interface card (NIC); the original Token Ring chip set is notorious for bottlenecks.

Where NICs in general are concerned, don't use 8-bit ones in file servers, where the most traffic is going to concentrate! They would probably be suitable for most workstations, though. It's quite possible, even with 8-bit cards, that data transfer is quicker over the cable than from your own local hard disk, due to the efficient way some servers operate.

Speed

Many products never meet with the commercial success they might expect because they're not perceived as being "fast" enough with respect to transmission speed.

It may seem important to salesmen, but speed is not actually that important. However fast your car may be able to go, you will still find yourself doing an average speed of 40-50 mph when travelling across country. So it is with networks, and a quoted throughput of 10 megabits per second is more likely to be 6 in practical terms (in fact, a "fast" system using CSMA may, in many cases, be significantly slower than one using "slow" ARCNet, due to the relative efficiencies with which data is transmitted).

Rather than making it run faster, you may be better off getting a faster hard disk or more RAM.

One effective way of getting optimum performance from a network without spending too much money is not to try and push too much data through it. Keep as many application and private data files as local as possible and use the servers for those which *must* be shared (this particularly applies to Windows, especially swap files). This way, you won't get too many traffic jams as the roads will be quieter.

Client/Server

This is a way of reducing traffic by changing the place at which program operation takes place. If you run a database on your workstation, not only would you probably load the program from the fileserver, but searches would take place there as well, so all your requests and their answers would be travelling over the cable, together with temporary files. However, if you moved the database to the server, so the searches take place there, only questions and answers would be transmitted.

Bandwidth Management

Otherwise, traffic capacity depends on bandwidth. Improve it by:

- **Adding more cable**, within the length limits allowed. For example, one way to improve on Token Ring is to have another cable going the other way round the circuit, so a packet can take the shortest route to its destination by selecting the appropriate line.

- **Splitting the network up** into segments at the server, and have an interface card for each segment (this is based on the thinking that the fewer users there are, the greater the effective bandwidth. As each segment improves, so does the network average). Then use the fileserver itself as a router to link the two (NetWare has excellent internal router software). A side benefit of this arrangement is an improvement in reliability, as one segment being down doesn't affect the other, but it also ensures that only traffic that needs to be in a particular place is actually there.

- **Providing a dedicated link**. For ten computers, this would normally mean 45 cables, but you can get the same effect with switching, where "dedicated links" are created on the fly in a switching box.

Bandwidth can be divided into a number of channels, and where this affects LANs is whether they are *baseband* or *broadband*.

Baseband

Baseband is a bandwidth with 0 Hz as the lowest frequency, having only one channel, thereby concentrating all its energy into one aspect, namely speed (this covers most LANs). Data is also transmitted directly, that is, in its raw state — it's not modulated in any way. Because all units use the same type of energy, only one signal at a time can travel along the cable.

Although potentially fast, the effective speed of baseband systems is slower than the official rating. With only one channel available, you can't retransmit on another one if there's a bottleneck, but have to wait till there's a gap.

Broadband

A broadband LAN can carry multiple channels on a single cable, so many communications can be active at the same time; more than 100 channels each, in fact, so this system compared to baseband is like a motorway compared to a country lane.

Because the overall bandwidth is subdivided into different ranges of frequencies (cable TV is one example), these networks require special tuning and strict procedures in order to work properly, which implies trained support staff.

Network Enhancers

There are certain devices you could add to a network to get better facilities or performance.

Mulitiplexers combine several data channels into one physical circuit with the combination and separation of signals occurring at both ends. Thus, they can be used between modems or over Mega-stream/Kilostream lines. There are two ways of multiplexing, with *Frequency* or *Time Division* (for further details see Chapter 3).

Synchronous vs Asynchronous

The network can be connected asynchronously or synchronously. Whether you use one or the other depends on your application. If you're only using internal Electronic Mail, then you probably don't need high speed, and asynchronous will do. On the other hand, if you're continually transferring lengthy documents you may be better off with synchronous. In fact, you may still need this if the volume of data is small, but is sent in rapid bursts; for instance, graphics applications don't need to send an awful lot of data, but do need it to hand quickly as screens are switched between drawings.

Hard Disks

One potential bottleneck in a network's performance is the hard disk. It may be a good move to use two smaller ones (or as many as possible) on the file server so as to split the load of requests for access. This will also give an improvement in system reliability and the security of having backups available.

Fault Tolerance and Data Security

What happens when the network doesn't run? Nobody works, of course, but, more importantly, the information in it is inaccessible when you may need to fulfil contracts or legal requirements.

How much of a disaster this will be depends on your circumstances, but most companies will have a *disaster recovery plan* which is geared to getting the network up and running again in as short a time as possible, even to the point of having a spare building available, although this is often shared with other companies. Again, how much you spend on this is up to you, but the quicker the recovery you need, the more it will cost.

However, the best way out of trouble is not to get into it in the first place. Many network operating systems now incorporate system fault tolerance features originally incorporated in NetWare. Fault Tolerance is a procedure used in many industries as a means of coping with equipment failure, which is accepted as a possibility, but not allowed to stop a system from running, such as with Aviation, where an aircraft will have dual (or triple) systems built in so that a flight can progress safely if one of them goes wrong. A good example in the computer world is the RAID system, described overleaf.

General SFT features include:

Disk mirroring	Two hard disks are used, with one being an exact copy of the other (hopefully not the bad sectors!) and constantly updated. Although both could fail, it's statistically rare.
Disk duplexing	This duplicates not just the disk, but the whole drive chain, including controllers, drives, interfaces and power supplies.
Transactional Tracking System	This ensures that *all* changes being made to a file are carried out, or none. It works by keeping a copy of the original data until the complete update has taken place; if it can't for any reason, the original data is replaced and the process aborted.
Hot fix	Data on damaged areas of the hard disk is automatically rewritten to a safe area set aside for the purpose. This is mainly a NetWare feature, but other software will make copies of the equivalent of the FAT and have them scattered about the place.

RAID

This stands for *Redundant Array of Inexpensive Disks*. It's a method of distributing data across a number of disks, so that it can be reconstructed after a disk failure. It uses techniques called *striping* and *mirroring* to do this; striping distributes data across many disks at the same time, whereas mirroring uses duplicate disk drives, each of which contain all the data.

Like an aeroplane with one engine out, you would get slightly less performance while one is out of commission, but life would otherwise continue normally until the faulty disk is replaced and brought up to date again. But if a second drive goes.....

There are 6 levels of RAID available; the three most popular (for PCs, anyway) are 1, 3 and 5.

- **Level 0** is basic striping using multiple disk heads. Restoration must be done from backup tapes if a disk fails, as data is not duplicated.

- **Level 1** includes Mirroring and Disk Duplexing, and is the most cost-effective for 4 Gb or less. Data can be read from alternate disks, depending on which one has the nearest head to the data.

- **Level 2** is designed for mainframes. Data is written a bit at a time to each disk in turn, with error codes to allow reconstruction being written to others.

- **Level 3** transfers all data in parallel to several data disks and only one for parity checking. Good for large blocks of data, such as graphics or image files, and is commonly used with the Macintosh.

- **Level 4** As for 3, but data is put on a block at a time.

- **Level 5** disks operate independently, with data and error recovery information spread across all the drives. Better suited to small-block transfers, as used in Netware file servers.

UPS

Uninterruptible Power Supplies sit between the mains and whatever equipment they feed, allowing electricity of whatever pedigree in, and nothing but a smooth supply out.

They work by allowing the mains to charge a battery inside, converting from AC to DC, then powering the computer through an *inverter*, which converts the DC back to AC. Their cost is directly proportional to how much current they supply and for how long, which can be anything from 5 minutes to an hour or a day. Whether you need one or not depends on how important your network is to you. One of the problems of running complex programs (particularly databases) is the inability to get back into them if they're not closed down properly, the same situation as if the power suddenly goes. This is usually because the equivalent of the File Allocation Table is not saved to disk (as it would be on a proper exit) and, quite understandably, the software can't find anything again.

Some networks have an ability to send signals to a UPS (over a serial cable), kick it into life and close down automatically in the proper manner.

5 minutes should be enough for everything to be closed down properly in case of a power breakdown. If you need more than about an hour, consider a generator instead.

With the fail-safe procedures built in to many systems, particularly with multiple copies of FATs and the like, a network used primarily for the simpler tasks may well survive without a UPS.

20

Software

The network operating system allows you to share resources and grant *access rights* to them. It also handles printing and communications in the background, if required. Provided the manufacturers stick to the OSI (or any other) model, any software should (theoretically) work with any hardware.

There are two types of software to consider; that which runs the network, and the application programs that do the work you require.

Application Programs

As far as the second type goes, as long as only one person is allowed to write to a particular file at a given time (although several may read it), that is, it supports *file locking*, it should be usable over a network. If you don't plan to share files, you can run anything, provided there's no copy protection that hates networks. You will need to tell the program where to find its related files, so that if it's invoked from an unexpected path, it doesn't get lost.

Apart from this, software used on a network is generally the same as normal, but additional licences will be needed to cater for the extra users (most companies just supply an extra disk to bump the original package up to the next grade).

Preventing Damage To Files

Simultaneous reading of files is not a problem (you would need this for the .EXE, .COM or .OVL files belonging to your program, for instance) but reading and writing together can cause any kind of trouble up to and including a system crash.

The most common problems arise when several people wish to use a data file at the same time or, more specifically, write to it simultaneously.

Although a DOS SHARE command allows a filename to be shared with a specified number of locks between application programs, this must be done every time the facility is required. Also, it doesn't keep track of who locked particular files. It does, however, allow an application program to lock a range of bytes in a file for exclusive use.

File Locking

It's worth noting first of all that file locking can cause problems of its own, in particular the *deadly embrace*, which occurs when users lock files that others need to finish their tasks. You could wait for ever for a file to become unlocked, particularly if there's a queue, like a house buying chain!

Wholesale file locking can also be inconvenient because some products restrict access to only one user at a time. On the other hand, some software allows multiple access to files, but no alterations until the original user has finished. A lot depends on how a program uses a file. Some load a file into memory, work on it and then close it. Others load a file, close it for safety and reopen it later to save the changes.

There are three versions of file locking commonly encountered:

- **None**. Used where just viewing takes place (and the file is marked as *Read Only*).

- **Shared**. Used where information may be extracted from a file (say for printing). Even though you're technically just viewing, it ensures the printout refelects the file's contents *at the time of printing*; shared locking prevents others from changing things in mid-print.

- **Exclusive**. If you want to change the file, you will need an *exclusive lock*, which prevents anyone else from doing anything that needs a lock – to use the previous example, printing while changes are being carried out. Similarly, you need to prevent writing to that file as well.

Locks can be *implicit*, that is, where the program assumes them based on your activity, or *explicit*, those that you consciously select.

Notifying Changes

Changes must be communicated to other users, and updated files must be circulated. Since even placing a lock on a file is an update, ways must be found of spreading the information around without clogging up the system.

The change could be made and the changes immediately sent to everybody, but this causes two problems:

- Other nodes that are due to receive the changes must be in a position to receive them, i.e. not doing anything else, which could be quite difficult on a busy network.

- Circulating changes increases the amount of traffic.

The file could be marked in a similar way to DOS, that is, in the file itself, or you could have a separate file to which any potential user must refer prior to going for the file required.

This is called a *lockfile*, of which you could have three, one for file information (status, etc), one for area information (which parts are locked) and one for update information (the changes actually made). Lockfiles not only keep track of who does what and to where, but, more importantly, who else knows about it; in other words, who has received the updates.

The deadly embrace can be resolved by the use of lockfiles, which are erased when finished with.

Operating Systems

Now, doing things backwards, we look at software that runs things, and the fact that MS-DOS is not much good as it stands for networks. It's hardly surprising, really, as it was never designed for the job in the first place. As such, it provides limited support for file sharing, even though versions 3.0 and above have had commands added to them that allow more software to be used on networks, such as ATTRIB (which can make files read-only for protection purposes), LASTDRIVE (that makes more drive designations available) and SHARE (which invokes file and record-locking capabilities).

DOS 3.3 added other networking facilities, such as APPEND (similar to PATH, but for data files as well), FASTOPEN (which caches filenames for quicker response) and SET HANDLE (which sets aside space for more open filenames).

Network operating systems emulate these facilities when required. More details will be found in *Product Overview* in Chapter 23.

Protocols

Just to recap, a protocol is a set of rules for transmission of data. Several have been developed over the years, and the most popular for network data transmission are described below.

NETBIOS

NETBIOS is a standard interface for networking PCs, written by IBM who designed the original for their PC LAN. It has the same function as the System BIOS, but for networking, consisting of drivers for simple hardware support.

NETBIOS allows PCs to communicate without needing a file server; applications can talk directly to the network through it rather than DOS. Many network operating systems have their own way of doing the same job, but can emulate NETBIOS if a program expects to use it. Don't expect to use any old thing that comes bundled with the software you want to use.

TCP/IP

Transmission Control Program (TCP) and Internet Program (IP) were used as standard protocols over the original Internet and its predecessors. Although only two are mentioned, it's actually made up of 5 core protocols. The other three are:

- **SMTP**. Simple Mail Transfer protocol. Handles basic E-mail, mailing lists, return receipts and forwarding.

- **FTP**. File Transfer Protocol. This is more sophisticated, consisting of *FTP Server* and *FTP Client* software, and is able to send files under user command.

- **TELNET**. Provides remote logon capabilities (e.g. terminal emulation), so a TCP/IP equipped PC can act as a terminal over a network to a Unix machine.

The **IP** part, which lives in all end systems and routers, acts as a relay, moving data between them; it takes care of packet addressing so a routing computer knows where to send to. The **TCP** part, on the other hand, only resides in end systems, checking on reliable delivery. It breaks down packets into smaller pieces and places them in sequence in a data envelope, which goes into an IP envelope. TCP/IP has four layers:

- **Network Access**. Contains protocols used to access a network, e.g. Ethernet, X.25, etc).

- **Internet**. Procedures required for data to traverse multiple networks (in other words, routing).

- **Transport**. Logic for ensuring reliable delivery of data between host systems. Also directs incoming mail.

- **Application**. Protocols for specific user applications.

TCP/IP is the most widely available and widely used set of protocols in its field, despite not being compatible with OSI. Alternative software incorporating TCP/IP includes *PC-NFS*, from SunSelect, and *PC/TCP* from FTP software, good for connectivity to Unix.

NFS, by the way, is the *Network Filing System*, which allows remote systems to act as file servers to dissimilar equipment.

IPX

Internetwork Packet eXchange; a protocol devised by Novell for its networks, whose purpose is to handle network packet routing, in that it directs network messages to the network card and out over the "Ether", in this case the cable joining the computers.

Netware workstations communicate directly with others via IPX, and although a "best effort" is made to deliver data packets, delivery is not guaranteed. The hit rate is over 98%, but if you're running a financial database, even this isn't good enough (see SPX).

Originally, it had to be generated specifically for each workstation's network card, with a program called WSGEN (that replaced SHGEN), but which is now replaced by the ODI architecture, which is much more flexible. Rather than being specific to a network card, the program reads a text file, NET.CFG, when it loads, so it knows what settings to use. Sample:

```
LINK DRIVER NE2000
    PORT 300
    INT 3
    MEM C8000*
    FRAME ETHERNET_802.3
    FRAME ETHERNET_II
```

* means optional (if your card needs it).

It actually sets up a notional (i.e. pretend) network card for each protocol you wish to use, and routes their data through the one physical card in your PC (up to 4 protocols per card). You can do it the other way, too, for better throughput.

There are three layers to ODI as used in a workstation, in the order of loading:

- **LSL,** or the *Link Support Layer.* This is what switches between the protocols loaded. Load this low (e.g. in base memory).

- **Lan Driver,** or the software to activate the NIC, such as NE2000.COM. Can be loaded high.

- **Protocol Stack,** such as IPXODI.EXE or TCPIP.EXE. IPXODI is split into IPX, SPX and RDR (Remote Diagnostics Responder), the latter two of which can be left out to save memory. Thus, IPXODI D = IPX + SPX and IPXODI A loads IPX only. Can be loaded high.

After the above have loaded, you need the *redirector software,* which would be NETX for IPX or TELNET for TCPIP. This enables DOS (or whatever) to access remote disks and printers which it cannot ordinarily do.

With NetWare 4, the equivalent for NETX is VLM, but it's only required if you want to use the *Global Naming* features.

Just add U to each of the above commands to unload them (LSL U).

SPX

SPX is otherwise known as Sequenced Packet eXchange, which guarantees packet delivery (unlike IPX) by ensuring that they arrive in the right order, and that their receipt is acknowledged. The receiving workstation has to respond with an acknowledgement that the data was received without error.

NETBEUI

The protocol used with LAN Manager or Windows for Workgroups. It is an extension of NETBIOS.

Appletalk

Appletalk is a baseband protocol which, in theory at least, can support up to 32 devices. There is a maximum bus length of 300m, though, due to the need to keep packet sizes down. It uses CSMA as a basis for operations, running at 230.4 kbits per second with twisted pairs and no dedicated file server. However, you will need a file server if you wish to operate a star system.

21

Using A Network

Using a network is quite easy; it's the concept that can be difficult for first time users. Mostly, you just use your computer as you would any other time, but because your computer is joined to others, you will find one or two differences, which are:

- A **log-on procedure**, which is the network's way of finding out who's using its facilities so it can allocate them fairly. It's also the *System Supervisor's* way of making sure that only those people who are allowed to use the network actually do so.

  Either you or your computer will be given a *username* that the network will recognise, together with a *password*, although the latter will depend on how paranoid they are about security. In some companies, you won't need one at all; in others, you will need one that is a minimum length and which is changed every few days.

  Similarly, when you quit working, you must remember to *logout* as well. Simple networks may not require any sort of logging on procedure.

- **Extra facilities**. You may be able to use several other printers (usually a long walk away!) and disk drives somewhere else in the building.

  You can load programs from these other drives, just as you can from your own, which will be given higher letters than the ones on your computer. For example, yours will be C:, and you can get to any of D: to Z: on the fileserver. The thing to remember is that *you can load and save work there, too*! If you save work to drive D:, that's where you must get it from next time; conversely, if you load it from there, that's where you save it.

- **Sharing Files**. Normally, you can do what you want with any data on your machine. With a network, files may be owned by somebody else, so there will be different levels of access based on who you are. For example, you might be able to *Read* files, *Write* to them, *Delete* them, or *Execute* them. It all depends on the privileges you are given and the permissions you are granted.

What you can actually do on the network depends on what the System Supervisor allows you to. The *Supervisor*, or *Network Manager* is responsible for the coordination and smooth running of the network (but see the next chapter for a closer look at what goes on).

You will most probably not be allowed past a sophisticated menu system, which will ensure that you can only get to parts of the whole network. If you are allowed to the *system prompt*, you will still be restricted to certain areas, or not allowed to do much when you get there. This comes under the heading of *privileges*, meaning what you are allowed to do in a particular area. If you are responsible for tape backups, for instance, you (or the software, which amounts to the same thing) will need to create temporary files, so you will be given *write privileges* for the job. You may even be given a temporary higher security clearance.

When printing, you may have to walk some way to get your work (although it may actually be delivered). Usually, your printing will be preceded by a nearly blank page containing just your username and some other details about your printing. This *banner page* is just to let other people know who it belongs to.

Another consideration concerns the storage space for your work. It's a great temptation, when you've got lots of room, not to delete the small files that get created from day to day. If left for too long, however, this could cause major congestion and slowing down of the hard disk as *fragmentation of files* takes place and it has to hunt around more for the information it wants. Get into the routine of regularly weeding the files you've created to get rid of the rubbish. Although the Supervisor will do most of the housekeeping, only you can identify the work you do from day to day.

Similarly, directory management in your private areas is usually your responsibility, as is backing up anything kept on your workstation.

Program Development

This, or other customising of applications may cause crashes and should be done off the network. If there's the remotest chance of a crash, you should work on your own.

Managing A Network

Once a company becomes dependent on computers, proper management of them becomes extremely important. Aside from protecting the information they contain, there needs to be some sort of discipline to ensure that the system is not overstrained and that those using it have a right to be there.

The Role of the Supervisor

The coordination and smooth running of a network of computers is the task of the *Supervisor*, or *Network Manager*.

The job includes *data security* in the form of proper backup procedures, as well as the more mundane tasks of allowing people on to the system, making it easy for them to use, and so on. In smaller companies, this may include adding machines and other hardware to the network, but there may well be a technical department to do this for you.

If there isn't, your job will essentially be split between setting up the system in the first place, and maintaining it thereafter. This chapter will assume you have a system already and deal mostly with maintenance, because this is how most supervisors come into the job. The network is usually inherited from somebody else, and you need to quickly get a grip on what they've been up to.

Supervising

On the network, you will have *Supervisor status*, which means that, amongst other things, you will:

- Decide what areas of the system people can get to.

- Determine whether they need passwords to get there.

- Restrict access to other areas.

- Load and update software.

- Maintain backups.

- Install new equipment and peripherals (maybe).

- Train users.

- Monitor network performance (e.g. check equipment and weed files).

- Keep yourself informed about new developments.

All of the above actually makes network supervision a full-time job. However, many companies will expect you to combine it with your normal duties (without training!).

Sometimes, you can delegate your authority and allow *Workgroup Managers* to do some of the above on your behalf. You will also need to appoint a deputy with equivalent security clearance to yourself.

Users

Users are the people served by the network or, in other words, those who use it as a tool in the course of their work. Generally, they should not be allowed outside the strict confines of a menu or batch file system that controls where they can go and what they can do there.

With proper automation, the network should be invisible to anyone using it. Users will only be interested in the services offered and not the technical details. All programs should work normally, with the only difference being that more facilities are available, particularly disk drives and printers, which won't be physically attached to their computers, but somewhere along the cable connecting them.

You can make life much easier for yourself by grouping people together and treating them as one unit (e.g. a *Group*) for administrative purposes.

Facilities

The facilities available to you as Supervisor include:

- Enabling and disabling user accounts.

- Specifying account expiration dates.

- Requiring user passwords, and specifying their lengths.

- Forcing periodic password changes.

- Forbidding the use of previously used passwords.

- Restricting logging on times. This is particularly useful in a university environment, for example, where different classes are allowed access to the computer facilities on a shift basis. The normal use, however, would be to restrict logons during a backup session, because open files won't be backed up. You could specify, for instance, that nobody logs on between 2200 and midnight whilst backing up takes place.

- Restricting logging on at particular workstations.

- Restricting concurrent connections (e.g. not logging on more than once at the same time).

- Restricting disk space used.

You don't have to use all of the above; they're just there in case you need them; what you get up to really depends on the size of your organisation and your local circumstances. As well as the above, the network checks periodically to ensure that each person has the right to continue being there. It does this by checking:

- Whether that person can log on during this time period.

- Whether the account has expired or has been disabled.

- Whether the account is out of funds (if applicable).

Security

Security can be difficult — on the one hand, you need a network that is open enough to share what it was set up for in the first place, and closed enough to guard against damage, loss and unauthorised access on the other.

If installed, *accounting systems* can keep track of who's using what and where. Some companies charge internally between departments for network facilities, and you can produce figures for this purpose, but it's also handy for keeping track of network performance and intruders, since all logins and logouts are kept track of. Each person's account keeps records of resources consumed. You can charge for server time used (the time logged in, or *connect time*), server disk space used, or for server requests (such as reading or writing files).

Otherwise, security revolves around *login procedures* and *rights of access*.

Rights of Access

You can allow or disallow access to files (or directories), and control what people can do with them once they get there by granting *privileges*; that is, you can allow people to operate in certain areas and work with files there up to certain levels.

Directory Level

Directory rights apply to the directory and any files and subdirectories in it. Typically, a user can:

Read	Read all files in a particular directory, or a single file.
Create	Create directories.
Write	Write to files
Erase	Delete directories or files.
Modify	Change attributes, or rename directories or files.

The ability to open a file is often assumed, but this may also be specifically granted.

File Level

File attributes provide further protection, which override directory level security. For example, even if somebody is allowed to delete files in a directory, a file marked as *Read-Only* is still safe.

Effective Rights

Effective rights are those that can actually be exercised by a user in a given directory, despite what is theoretically granted (see above).

Viruses

Networks can be secure from viruses, but not under all circumstances. If users have permission to modify files, then so has any virus brought in by them; Supervisor privileges (that is, the ability to do *anything*) will also be transferred. In view of this, don't use the "Supervisor" username all the time — create one for yourself for your day to day work that has lesser privileges, just in case.

Product Overview

What follows is a short selection of network operating systems that are available. The list is not conclusive, and inclusion does not imply a recommendation, but it is some sort of guidance in a market with so many similar items. There are several good products that can't be included, either because of lack of space or the sheer pace of technology.

Some are heavyweights, used where a LAN may be a cost-effective alternative to installing a minicomputer; in other words, an *enterprise wide* solution. As such, reliability, speed, security and high performance are more important considerations than cost, and will therefore be outside the scope of most readers of this book. It's worth knowing that they exist, though, as many humbler products use features obtained from them, and little acorns.......

As the notes below have been gleaned from a mixture of experience and product information, check out what you want before you buy it! Not only could this save you from buying rubbish, you may find something that's an absolute gem but not well known.

Products can be divided into three groups:

- **Low cost,** with basic facilities, e.g. E-mail and resource sharing. They have minimum security and performance, and are peer-to-peer. Cabling is twisted pair, or coax.

- **Medium price**; limited versions of high cost networks, which may need a dedicated server, or at least a powerful machine somewhere. Reasonable security and accounting.

- **High-end**. Do everything, but need equipment to match. May use SFT, disk mirroring, and the like.

Products can also be divided into two groups:

- **Proprietary**, or *server based*, which ignore DOS and do things their own way, as a result of which they provide high performance and security, as everything is controlled centrally. Unfortunately, they can be inflexible for the same reason (it's difficult to share peripherals on individual workstations). The classic is NetWare.

- **DOS-based**, and typically *peer-to-peer*. These run DOS, then the networking software, so you may have to watch memory requirements. They don't make best use of the equipment available (see *NetWare*, below, for why), but faster processors, better DOS and cacheing have largely masked this. Designed for *workgroup computing*, where a group of people wish to communicate with each other all the time, but only occasionally outside.

Server Based

Server-based networks consist of one or more servers, through which all the traffic from the attached workstations goes.

NetWare

NetWare was originally developed around the Motorola 68000 processor. At that time, this particular device had nothing like DOS (or even CP/M) that could be used with it, so Novell wrote something of their own from scratch. This was done in C, so it was easily portable when PCs based on Intel's x86 chips became more popular.

However, since the idea was for multi-users to be multi-tasking, Novell had to bypass the PCs hardware instructions if they wanted an effective fileserver. This is because the PC was designed for single user, single tasking applications.

Netware is an operating system in its own right, which means that you don't need DOS or Unix before you can load it (though it will run as a task under OS/2). Version 2 works on 286s, 3 on 386s and above, as does 4. Version 4 is better than the others at multi-server networking and WAN connectivity.

It works with Ethernet, Token Ring and ARCNet, together with protocols such as IPX/SPX, NETBIOS, AFP, TCP/IP and FTP.

As NetWare talks directly to the PC's components, DOS is unable to use the hard disk drives, but Novell uses them more efficiently anyway.

The Hard Disk

DOS allocates space on a disk sequentially, where sectors are used one after the other, so you have to trawl through the whole lot from the beginning every time you want something, because only forward searches are allowed in the File Allocation Table (or FAT), which is what DOS calls the index of a disk. If the next request from block 900 is for data on block 899, then the search starts again at block 1 instead of merely going backwards one sector — this can happen each time a request is made!

NetWare, on the other hand, uses *elevator seeking*, which allocates priorities to disk accesses according to where they are, coordinating disk head movements so that data can be collected or delivered *en route* to other places, rather in the same way that an elevator will stop to collect people on the seventh floor whilst going up to the tenth. This can increase disk throughput by anything up to 50%.

Disk *writing* is also separated from *reading*, which allows the former to become a background task for completion during quiet periods. Data is stored in a *cache block* until that block is full or a certain period has gone by, so all the write requests for the same area of the disk are serviced at the same time.

Disk Cacheing

Many applications use the same files over and over again, and it makes sense to try and store these in memory to make access quicker. NetWare monitors the parts that are used most often and gives them priority storage space.

Most of NetWare's memory is used for cacheing, so if you're short of memory, the amount used for other system purposes may have to be reduced. For versions prior to 4, memory used for cacheing should be between 40-60% of total memory, and never less than 20%. It doesn't help, with NetWare, to use a hardware cache on the server; in fact, it will slow things down.

A useful side-effect of cacheing of whatever sort is the reduction in *file fragmentation*, which is the usual cause of hard disks losing their performance edge. Thus, the more memory you have for cacheing, the less the effects of fragmentation you will suffer.

VINES

A heavyweight, this one, in the same league as NetWare, and based on minicomputer procedures (VINES is short for *VI*rtual *NE*tworking *S*ystem). It really only comes alive on something like a 32-bit server, running on top of AT&T UNIX, although there is a variant for the SCO version.

On a 386-based machine, it needs a minimum of 8 Mb RAM. It supports Ethernet, Token Ring and ARCNet, with protocols such as TCP/IP, Appletalk, IPX/SPX, NETBIOS and FTP (their own version).

It's always been good for Wide Area Networking, and is mentioned briefly because it's a good example of a powerful system, but really outside the scope of this book. Further details, if required, from Banyan Systems Inc, in the USA.

LAN Manager

Runs on top of OS/2, Unix or Windows NT, all of which needs lots of memory, hard disk space and horsepower to equal NetWare's performance (speed was never this product's strong point). It's licensed to many OEM's, including DEC, HP, SCO and NCR.

It supports Ethernet, Token Ring and ARCNet, together with NETBEUI (preferred for smaller networks) and TCP/IP.

It uses "Domains", which are conceptually similar to workgroups. Each domain may contain several servers, and once you log into one domain, you are automatically logged in to each server in it, which saves you talking to each one individually.

Windows NT

Designed to be a workgroup server. Supports NETBEUI, TCP/IP, and is compatible with NetWare and Vines. Needs 16 Mb RAM and up to 70 Mb hard disk space.

NT Server

LAN Manager integrated with NT. Resource hungry. Adds RAID, Remote Access and support for Appletalk, Vines, DEC Pathworks, IBM LAN Server, SNA, WFW, NetWare and TCP/IP.

Peer to Peer

This is where several computers of similar status share the operation of the network and the provision of services.

Windows For Workgroups

This naturally provides the best integration for Windows, but needs the proper hardware. It doesn't have much security, but it will co-reside quite happily with more security oriented networks, such as NetWare, or LanTastic!. It provides E-mail (for DOS clients as well, with extra software) and fax sharing.

You must designate the resources to be shared first (through *File Manager* for directories and files, and *Print Manager* for printers) on the relevant machines, *then* allocate them on the machines that require to use them.

Windows for Workgroups stems from LAN Manager, and at least has SMB/NETBEUI and TCP/IP in common as protocols with products such as Digital's *Pathworks*.

ARCNet users won't be able to use Novell networks simultaneously; when required, ARCNet packets are encapsulated in Ethernet ones and unwrapped at the destination, but NetWare cannot handle the unwrapping.

Little Big LAN

A powerful RS232 network, but it will also use Ethernet, ARCNet, modems and parallel ports. One machine can act as a gateway between the types, which is useful for connecting laptops. It's basic, but cheap, so you need some knowledge to set it up properly.

LANTastic!

A DOS-based LAN that is good for mixing older machines (even XTs) with newer ones and the inevitable Windows. Capable of operating very large networks indeed (up to 500 and more). Good security and E-mail. Can talk to Macs, and a Lantastic! server can be used as a bridge into a NetWare network.

The /AI version is *Adapter Independent*, which means you can use a selection of NICs, as opposed to Artisoft's own.

Personal NetWare

Successor to *NetWare Lite*, which was intended to be an easy introduction to NetWare proper although, naturally, it was nowhere near as powerful.

It comes free with Novell DOS (but runs under any DOS), and provides file transfer, printer sharing, security, etc, with a single login facility for real NetWare. Reasonably powerful, but hasn't got the market share that LANTastic! has. Novell DOS provides multitasking, though.

Appletalk

One convenience of Apple products is that networking ability (in the hardware at least) is built in, and that includes printers.

Appletalk runs on other machines as well, though, and Appletalk adapter cards are available for the IBM PC and compatibles, amongst several others.

You can use Appletalk based equipment on something like Ethernet, but you will need some sort of converter (e.g. Kinetics' *FastPath*) or a bridge.

Appleshare

The Mac is able to serve as the centre of a network as well. Appleshare uses a Mac as a file server for combinations of up to 32 Macs and PCs.

Remote Access

This is software that allows you to connect over long distances and remotely control another computer. File transfer services will typically be provided as well. The computer being called is the *host*, and the caller is the *remote*, or *client*.

Normally, the host should be left on permanently, with software loaded waiting for a call to come in. For PCs, *PcAnywhere*, *Carbon Copy*, or *Co/Session* spring to mind, and for Apples, there is *Apple Remote Access Client*, which allows you to mount remote volumes as icons in the same way you do it from your local network.

24

Troubleshooting

Problems are usually quite simple, although they never seem so at the time! Fault finding should be done in a logical way, following a definite procedure, which may at times seem a long way round, but is actually shorter in the long run.

Establish a process of elimination, starting with the big picture, so you don't limit yourself. This means starting with the whole system first, then working downwards by cutting the problem in half every time. For example, if your printer is not producing what you expect, try it with another PC; if that works, then you're left with the PC, on which you can try changing the software. If that's OK, then it's a hardware problem on the PC, and so it goes on.

You should always try to work with probabilities rather than prejudice, as good troubleshooting needs a completely open mind. For example, you could say that a particular hard disk is probably the cause of the present trouble, because it's got a track record, but still look at the rest of the system. If you were prejudiced, you would close your mind to other possibilities, just change the hard disk and waste a lot of time in the wrong area.

Don't assume that just because something has worked well up till now, that it will continue to do so. On the other hand, troublesome items may well, for once in their lives, be performing as they should.

Aids To Diagnosis

Self Tests

A self-test is a procedure whereby the equipment concerned tests itself internally, the successful passing of which is supposed to indicate that all is well inside. For example, a common one for printers is to hold down the *Line Feed* button while turning the thing on. When you let go of the button, the printer should demonstrate what it's capable of.

Unfortunately, few of these procedures actually test everything – a self-test on a modem may not test all of the RS232 pins, only the most commonly used. It may also only tell you that a bulb is working, as opposed to the whole circuit. Wherever you can, use external test procedures, either as a substitute or as a backup for self-testing. RS232 sockets as a whole can be tested with a *breakout box*, of which more in a moment.

Loopbacks

In a loopback test, the output of any item is routed straight back into the system on the return path and the results at both ends are compared. You can do this first with the computer, then do it with a modem attached, then do it with the line which the modem is on, then put the other modem on, and so on.

For the computer, you need a *loopback connector*, which is a plug of the type normally used, but wired in such a way that signals can be sent to and received from a communications port without anything being connected to it.

Try this wiring for a 25-pin RS232 D-sub connector:

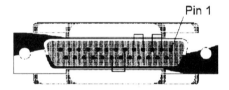

The pins without wires are unconnected. With this attached, what you type should appear directly on the screen – it's good for testing terminals.

A word of caution needs to be inserted here, as well. Most analogue circuits are designed to operate with a substantial difference in signal level from input to output – this is so that the difference between a 1 and a 0 is known. Usually the output signal is lower than the input, and the difference could be anything up to 16 decibels.

If you perform a loopback (that is, routing the output straight back in to the input), this difference in signals will be immediately apparent and the input signal will be vastly different from what it should be. This could cause receiving equipment to operate improperly and give false signals.

Systems that have loopback tests built in sort this out automatically, but something other than a loopback should be used otherwise (maybe an assistant at the other end to compare results).

Modems

On a Hayes-compatible modem, one of the registers will have a variety of self-test modes which, when activated, perform analogue loopback tests on the modem (or a remote modem) by turning the transmitter to the same frequency as used by the receiver.

The code for this is

```
AT S16=1 C1 D
```

assuming you're in originate mode and register S16 covers the test. The response will be

```
CONNECT
```

with all transmitted data echoed back to your screen. Don't forget to clear properly.

Monitors And Analysers

You can monitor the traffic in a network with software or hardware based tools. *Protocol Analysers* can look at the traffic and pinpoint congestion, signal retransmissions, timeouts, response times and general performance but, since the cost is high, probably overkill for small networks. The most well known is *The Sniffer*.

Network Management Systems (NMS) are software based, and typically run from a workstation, from where interrogations can be made of devices (e.g. bridges, hubs, routers, workstations or servers) which must be running *agent software*, that replies to regular interrogations from the NMS. They include:

- **SNMP** *Simple Network Management Protocol* (actually, it's the protocol that's simple).

- **CMIP**. *Common Management Information Protocol*, which comes from ISO.

- **NETVIEW**, from IBM.

- **PolyCenter**, from DEC.

Cable Testers

These attach to a cable and tell you most things about it quite quickly. For example, they can inform you about attenuation, noise, crosstalk, etc. You could always use a multimeter (see below), but this naturally takes longer. Then again, it's cheaper.

Breakout Box

A small box which has an RS232 socket at each end and Light Emitting Diodes (LEDs) and a means of crossing wires in the middle. You place it between the devices at either end of the cable you have a problem with and set things in motion.

The LEDs indicate the presence or not of output or input and you can swap the leads or short-circuit them until you get the wiring arrangement you want. Then you just get a lead made up to those specifications. Don't forget to turn the switches *off* on those leads that you short circuit or cross over.

Multimeters

Although cheap, these are quite useful, if a little slow to use, especially for checking voltage levels and resistances. A good example is detecting cable problems in conjunction with terminators on coax cable. Terminators contain a resistor that connects the core and the shield, placing them in parallel and making the effective resistance half the value. The resistance between the core and the screen at any workstation should therefore be about 25 ohms for Ethernet, allowing 2-3 ohms per 100 feet from the terminator.

If the cable is open, you'll get 50 ohms instead. At this point, take off a terminator and see if the resistance changes. If so, the cable is good on that side. With it still off, move in the other direction, and when you read 50 ohms again, you've just gone past the open circuit.

Sundries

The usual odds and ends around a workshop:

- Mains testers.

- Cheapo AM radio, to check for cable radiations.

- MAU testers. These make sure the relays don't stick.

Modems

Let's have a look at some of the more obvious things first:

- Have you paid your phone bill?

- Have you got the modem connected to the serial port (and not confusing it with the printer?). Is your software sending to the same port? This can be done with the MODE command in MS-DOS or the STAT command in CP/M, if not.

- Is your cable "straight through" for the modem, and a null modem cable otherwise?

- Is it connected to the phone line?

- Is it switched on?

- Is only one device trying to use the COM port? (i.e. you haven't got an interrupt clash—see *Expansion Cards*, below) be careful with COM 3 and COM 4, which share IRQ 4 and IRQ 3 with COM 1 and COM 2, respectively. DOS was never designed for these, and different software has different ideas about how to use them.

- What lights are showing when you turn your modem on? You should expect to see at least DTR, RTS and CTS once your software has loaded.

- Are you operating in Full Duplex, or whatever the receiver is expecting, and are you in Originate mode?

Some software (particularly Sage *ChitChat*) requires all connections to be properly made, since its operation depends on the status of the lines. If one is loose, nothing will happen at all.

Otherwise, one of the first places to start is the transmission speed. These must both be the same at each end, as must be:

- The number of bits per word (7 or 8, usually).

- The number of stop bits (try 1).

- Parity (none).

The above will either be set up with software or by a selection of DIP switches on the modem, which usually live in a small plastic box about an inch long.

If you're connecting, but still not getting through, then things are a bit more serious. Try pressing < Esc > or sending a carriage return (some systems require two in quick succession to wake them up. Sometimes this just toggles them through speed changes until they match yours).

However, if you are getting results, but it's gobbledegook, it's almost certainly the speed or parity. Go for the latter if about half the characters are recognisable (try 7 bits and even parity). Recheck your settings first, but if you've connected and are still getting strange characters, try dropping the baud rate down one speed. If the text makes some sense, but has a lot of strange symbols and numbers embedded, try using an ANSI terminal emulation.

If your modem dials, but obviously hasn't caught the line (i.e. you can still hear the dialling tone after the numbers have been sent), try changing the dialling method from *Tone* to *Pulse*. You may need to combine Pulse and Tone dialling on some exchanges, such as pulse dialling the 9 to get the outside line, then using Tone for the rest. Just place a **T** after the 9.

Also, check the cable to the telephone socket, especially with cheap internal modems and conversions from American to British. The data carrying wires on the American (RJ11) type go on the inside, and the ones on the British to the second ones in from the outside. The ones you get from Tandy don't work!

The remote modem may not be working to the same standard – you may be calling an American system without sending the expected Bell tones, or calling a European one without using CCITT procedures. If using a Hayes modem, you can get it to "blind dial" by setting the **ATX** command (X1 or X3).

If you're trying to connect to a V.32*bis* modem with a V.22*bis* one, you need to be aware the answer tones are different. V.32*bis* modems use phase reversals every half second that may confuse the speed sensing circuitry in the other one. You can get around this by forcing the modem to a particular speed. Try **ATF5** to set 2400.

You can also do a more extensive check on your (Hayes) modem with software. Connect everything up except the telephone lines, and go into terminal mode. An initialisation string will be sent from the terminal and you can therefore expect a reply from the modem. If you issue the command **AT** by itself, you should get **OK** back (check that the same characters as you type appear on the screen), otherwise you will be told that nothing is connected.

The command **AT A** should get you a high pitched tone (if you've got a speaker). If you type anything, the tone should stop and **NO CARRIER** appear on the screen. Issuing **ATDT1234** will get a dialling sound from the modem, and **ATH1** when connected to **LINE** a dialling tone. **ATH0** will hang up.

If you get the **CONNECT** signal, then **NO CARRIER**, the modem is probably dropping the line when when the computer drops DTR, (e.g. the modem is not getting a DTR). You could enable DTR permanently (with software or hard wiring the cable) or using **AT&D0** to disable this feature entirely.

WWhheenn yyoouurr cchhaarraacctteerrss aappeeaarr ttwwiiccee, it means that you're in half duplex and *local echo* is on — what you send is being echoed to the screen as well as what the remote host sends back as part of its echoplex error-checking procedure. Switch to Full Duplex or turn local echo off. Conversely, you need to switch this on if you're getting no characters at all on the screen when you type.

Fax Modems

Fax software writers tend to assume that nothing else will use the equipment, so may not reset the modem properly once they've finished. A command that *may* fix this is **AT + FCLASS = 0**, which could be added to an initialisation string. It doesn't always work.

If you want to find out what type of modem you have (e.g. class 1 or 2, type **AT + FCLASS = ?**. The answer **0,1** means class 1 and **0,2** means class 2.

Continual Reconnections

"Call Waiting" services don't actually issue an engaged signal, but use a plastic voice to tell you that the line is busy. The beeps that are used to tell the engaged person that someone is calling can confuse a modem, so it's a good idea to turn off Call Waiting before transmitting. This is done with **#43#**. Turn it on again with ***43#**.

In the USA, ***70** turns it off for one call, so you can issue it with your modem commands.

In summary, if your communicating is not proceeding as expected, you have several choices:

- Incorrect modem installation and configuration.

- The same for software.

- And the serial port (you may have two COM ports).

- Wrong dialling method (tone instead of pulse).

- Poor line quality.

- Poor cable connections.

- Incompatibility with connecting service.

Printers and Terminals .....

If you get garbage, go straight for the baud rate and parity. Text instead of graphics means that 8-bit ASCII needs to be set at both ends. Getting garbage presupposes that your cable is OK (it must be pretty near if you're getting anything at all), but check it anyway.

Networks

Prevention is always better than cure and networks are no exception. Continuous monitoring is needed to ensure everything's working OK and to check whether saturation point is being approached, to the point that new devices will be needed to cope with it all.

Some network operating systems provide utilities to help find problems, which include reports of bad packets and network errors.

If you do encounter some problems, check the cabling in particular, even if you have used a self-test. After checking that everything is on, make sure that every wire in every junction box is positioned properly and that every screw is tight, particularly T-pieces and the BNC connections (cheap T-pieces have been known to crack under pressure, as have network managers). The military spec ones are the best. Check all connections between interface boards, jack sockets, transceivers and/or junction boxes.

You may also be using the wrong frame type; NetWare 3.12, for example, defaults to 802.2, whereas previous products used 802.3.

Expansion Cards

Expansion cards use four methods of communicating with the rest of the computer:

- Direct Memory Access (DMA).

- Base Memory Address.

- I/O port address.

- Interrupt Setting (IRQ).

Direct Memory Access (DMA)

High speed devices on the expansion bus are allowed to place their data directly into memory over reserved *DMA channels* without having to go through the CPU. The process will be controlled by a DMA controller chip, which is prone to burning out if run too fast (it's linked to bus speed, which can be adjusted through your Advanced Chipset Setup).

There are several channels available for DMA, and typically you would use use numbers 1 or 3 for NICs (though not often). This table lists DMA channels in AT compatibles:

DRQ No	Device	Notes
0	system	8-bit
1		8-bit
2	Floppy controller	System
3		8-bit
4	Slave DMA input	16-bit
5		16-bit
6		16-bit
7		16-bit
8		System

Not many NICs use DMA, but the 3COM Etherlink II does. Try DMA 3 on an AT, or DMA 2 on an XT.

Base Memory Address

Expansion cards often contain small amounts of memory to act as buffers for temporary data storage when the computer is busy. Alternatively, the card may have a ROM containing instructions the card needs to operate, in our case a Remote Reset PROM.

The upper 384K of the first megabyte of memory is reserved for private use by the computer, so that any expansion cards with their own memory or ROMs can operate safely there without interfering with programs in base memory, or *vice versa*.

This *Upper Memory Area* is split into regions, A-F, which in turn are split into areas numbered from 000 to FFF hexadecimally (Upper Memory locations are always expressed in hexadecimal—640K translates to A0000). With the right software, this area can also be converted into *Upper Memory Blocks* for use by TSRs, or memory-resident programs. The *Base Memory Address* indicates the starting point of a range of memory used by the card.

Below is a map of how the memory space above 640K (A0000) is used on many computer systems.

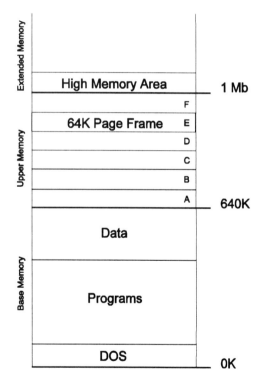

Actually, upper memory starts halfway through Area C. The bit from A000-C7FF is actually base memory that has been grabbed by the video adapter, some of which is reclaimable if you don't want to use graphics. The ROM BIOS will use area F, so the *useable* upper memory area is typically areas D and E (with, occasionally, the first part of Area F, sometimes only used in the initial stages of boot up).

```
A0000-AFFFF EGA/VGA video memory
B0000-B7FFF Mono video memory
B8000-BFFFF RGB and mono video memory
C0000-C7FFF EGA/VGA BIOS ROM
C8000-CFFFF XT hard disk BIOS ROM (can vary)
D0000-DFFFF Expansion RAM (LIM) area (varies)
E0000-EFFFF Expansion RAM /some EISA BIOS
F0000-FFFFF System BIOS-1st page available?
```

What address in Upper Memory to use for your card (that is, the *Lowest Free Address*) initially depends on the video card, e.g.

```
Video type   LFA

Hercules     C000
EGA          C400
VGA          C800
```

As an example, the video ROM typically occupies the area C000-C7FF, so the Lowest Free Address for another card is C800.

However, C800 is also a good choice for (16K) hard disk controller ROMs in ISA or EISA machines, so if you have a VGA card as well, you wouldn't normally expect to use anything lower than CC00.

Using a base address of D0000 as an example, here are the ranges of memory occupied by a ROM or adapter RAM buffer:

```
ROM size     Range used

8 K          D0000-D1FFF
16 K         D0000-D3FFF
32 K         D0000-D7FFF
```

Base I/O Address

I/O addresses (I/O = Input/Output) act as "mailboxes", or simply locations where messages can be passed between components; they are 1K wide openings in memory that relate to the data bus, also expressed in hexadecimal.

The *Base* I/O Address is the first of a *range* of addresses rather than a single one; for example, most network adapters use a range of 20h, so 360h really means 360h-37Fh (in which case watch for LPT 1, whose base is 378).

COM 1 reserves a range of addresses from 3F8h to 3FFh, which are used for various tasks, like setting up speed, parity, etc.

The table below shows reserved I/O addresses.

000-01F	DMA controller 1
020-03F	Interrupt controller 1
040-05F	System timers
060-06F	PPI controller and keyboard
070-07F	CMOS Clock (AT)
080-087	DMA page registers
089-09F	DMA page registers
0A0-0BF	Interrupt controller 2 (AT & PS/2)
0C0-0DF	DMA controllers (ATs & PS/2)
0E0-0EF	Real-time clock (PS/2 30)
0F0-0FF	Maths coprocessor
1F0-1F8	AT Hard disk controller
200-20F	Game port
210-21F	
220-22F	NetWare Key Card (very old, this)
230-23F	Bus mouse
240-24F	
250-25F	
260-26F	
270-27F	LPT3 (278-27B; LPT 2 in the XT)
280-28F	LCD display on Wyse 2108 PC
290-29F	
2A0-2AF	
2B0-2BF	
2C0-2CF	
2D0-2DF	
2E0-2EF	COM 4 (2E8-2EF) GPIB adapter 0
2F0-2FF	COM 2 (2F8-2FF)
300-30F	Most NICs default setting
310-31F	
320-32F	Hard disk controller (XT)
330-33F	
340-34F	
350-35F	
360-36F	
370-37F	LPT 2 (AT-378-37B)
380-38F	SDLC/Secondary BISYNC I/face
390-39F	
3A0-3AF	
3B0-3BF	Mono display/printer adapter
3BC-3BF	LPT 1
3C0-3CF	EGA/VGA adapter
3D0-3DF	CGA/EGA/VGA adapter
3E0-3EF	COM 3 (3E8-3EF)
3F0-3F7	Floppy drive controller
3F8-3FF	COM 1

Note that some of the above may vary according to your machine's architecture, especially COM 3 and COM 4.

Computers with a small built-in LED or LCD display (to show disk cylinder data or clock speed, for example) might use certain I/O addresses for that display.

Interrupt Setting

If any part of the computer needs to talk to the Central Processor, it will usually have to interrupt it so that the CPU can stop what it's doing to attend to the new situation. Technically, an interrupt transfers program execution from one place to another (like GOTO in a batch file). On a PC, it's a convenient way of calling subroutines from DOS or the BIOS. Several levels of interrupt capability are provided, and each one is given a different priority; thus the keyboard has a higher priority than the mouse, and any input from the keyboard is dealt with first in any competition between the two.

A hardware interrupt is caused by a signal from a hardware device, such as a mouse or printer, and a software interrupt will be originated by a program.

The *Interrupt ReQuest Line* is used by a device to grab the CPU's attention. XTs have eight IRQ levels; ATs and PS/2s have two sets of eight. An interrupt controller chip allocates priorities and interrupts what the CPU is doing to service the device, passing interrrupts on to the CPU one at a time, as the CPU itself only has one interrupt line.

The lower the IRQ level, the higher the priority the associated device is given. For example, COM 1, which uses IRQ 4, is typically programmed to interrupt the CPU any time an incoming character is received, but if it tries to do this while the keyboard is using IRQ 1, it will have to wait its turn.

However, where a system has a dual interrupt controller (e.g. ATs, PS/2s, 386 and 486 machines) IRQ levels 8 to 15 have priority over levels 3 to 7, because the second controller's line is wired to IRQ 2 on the first chip. This makes IRQ 2 more complex to service and should be avoided for that reason.

If you're using an EISA or Micro Channel machine, you may come across *arbitration levels*, which work in a similar way.

Classic symptoms of interrupt conflicts include colour screens mysteriously turning black and white, machines hanging up when certain programs load, and mouse problems.

This table shows IRQ lines assigned (in the AT), in order of priority:

```
IRQ    Device

0      System timer
1      Keyboard
2      Slave interrupt controller

8      Real-time clock
9      Redirected to IRQ 2
10
11
12     Mouse
13     Maths coprocessor
14     Hard disk controller
15

3      COM 2/COM 4
4      COM 1/COM 3
5      LPT 2
6      Floppy controller
7      LPT 1
```

Many cards use IRQ 5 as a default (it's usually used for LPT 2:). As printing isn't interrupt-driven, you may be able to use IRQ 7, provided nothing strange is hanging off the parallel port (tape sreamers sometimes do).

Boards with 8-bit edge connectors are limited to IRQ 3-7 or 9 only.

Appendix A

Instant NetWare

This is a quick guide to NetWare for those of you lumbered with a network to look after and little prospect of being trained for it (it happens, believe me!). It's only meant to be an introduction to the concepts involved in running NetWare, so at least you will get a fighting chance of finding out what's going on. It should be read in conjunction with Chapter 22, *Managing A Network*.

Drive Mappings

If you have a single-user background, you are no doubt used to the idea that floppy disk drives come in two flavours, A and B, and that everything else is allocated names upwards from C, which is usually the first hard disk. In other words, a physical storage device is described by a letter.

The good news is that NetWare doesn't do things this way! Sure enough, your floppies will still be A: and B:, and local hard drives anything up to E:, but other drive letters will refer to a *directory path on the server's hard disk*, and not a physical device as such; a "logical drive", in other words, one that doesn't really exist, but may as well do for all the difference it makes. So, when your users log on to drive F:, as far as they're concerned, there is such a drive, but you and I both know that it's only pretend and they've really latched on to a path on the file server's hard disk (all of which will become clearer shortly).

The first available network drive's letter, by the way, will depend on the LASTDRIVE setting in your workstation's CONFIG.SYS file. If this is E:, then you login on drive F:, as described above. If it is P:, then you would start at drive Q:. Clear? As mud, probably, but read on, it gets worse!

The fileserver's NetWare hard disk partition (you can have a DOS one as well, for booting up with) is divided up into *volumes* that are given names. The first one is always called SYS: (short for SYStem), because this is where the NetWare operating system files are kept. On a small network it's quite common to put your program and data files in that volume as well, but it's not a good idea.

If, for any reason, the system files get corrupted, you won't be able to get at your data without considerable difficulty, if at all. It's far better to split the hard disk up into separate volumes (say one for each department of the company), and keep only NetWare in SYS:. Then, if you get a problem, you only need to run INSTALL, reconstruct that volume and the others will be found automatically (with NetWare 3.1x and above).

When the fileserver starts, each volume on the hard disk is *mounted* in turn (you cannot delete a volume without *dismounting* it first).

Each volume contains subdirectories, and we are back on familiar territory, except that now you allocate drive letters to pathnames, which is known as *Drive Mapping*. It's very similar to the way the SUBST command works in DOS, in that you can take a directory path and substitute it with a spare drive letter, to save you typing the whole lot out when you want to change to that directory.

For example, to allocate drive letter F: to SYS:PUBLIC, you would type (from a workstation, having logged on):

```
MAP F:=SYS:
```

Every time you log on to F:, you will actually be in the \PUBLIC directory in the SYS: volume.

MAP commands can be placed in a *login script* (of which more later) so they can be established every time a user logs in. It's even possible to allocate different paths to the same drive letter based on the user's *login name*, done with the equivalent of environment variables (X: is usually the drive letter allocated to a user's private directory).

There are four directories automatically set up inside SYS: during installation, and they are:

      SYS:SYSTEM   Never usually touched by users.

      SYS:PUBLIC   For the main bulk of user programs.

      SYS:MAIL   For user' s E-mail.

      SYS:LOGIN   Where users are allowed to login from.

So if you wanted to map the letter G: to the MAIL directory, you would type:

```
MAP G:=SYS:MAIL
```

Note the semi-colon in between SYS and MAIL. It's always used after the volume name. If you went further down the structure, you would use the traditional backslash:

```
MAP G:=SYS:MAIL\FRED
```

Where FRED is the private directory of the user FRED.

There are three types of drive mapping. *Network drive mappings* happen after the manner described above, in that you assign a letter to represent a route to the information you want. *Local drive mappings*, on the other hand, relate to complete drives on the workstation.

A *search drive mapping* (of which there can be up to 16) acts in the same way as the PATH command in DOS, giving the computer a standing instruction where to look for your files before it tells you it can't find what you want. The difference is that MAP reacts to data files as well as program files, unlike DOS, whose PATH command only acts on .BAT, .EXE or .COM ones (so MAP combines the functions of APPEND as well, which is useful for large databases).

The complete list of drive mappings appears on the screen when you login, somewhat like this:

```
Good morning, SUPERVISOR

Drive A    maps to a local disk
Drive B    maps to a local disk
Drive C    maps to a local disk
Drive D    maps to a local disk
Drive E    maps to a local disk

Drive F:= [servername]/SYS:SYSTEM
Drive G:= [servername]/SYS:MAIL
Drive H:= [servername]/SYS:LOGIN

SEARCH1:=Z:[servername]/SYS:PUBLIC
SEARCH2:=Y:[servername]/SYS:PUBLIC\DOS
```

SEARCH2 has been mapped to a directory on the file server containing an operating system (i.e. DOS), where all users can obtain it. Thus, it doesn't take up space on their hard drives. You can improve this by using variables:

```
PUBLIC/%MACHINES/%OS/%OS_VERSION
```

where % represents a variable name that you can point to, making it easy to have several types of DOS available. The above would translate to:

```
PUBLIC/IBM/DOS/3.3
```

If you need to see what's what at any other time, just type MAP followed by **< Return >**.

There is a convention for drive naming, where the first 5 drive letters (out of the 26 available) are for local drives, and the remainder are for network drives, working forwards. If left to itself, NetWare will create search drive mappings from Z: and work backwards, so that there is as large a spread as possible between the two types:

A-E	Local drives.
F	Network home drive (SYS:).
G-L	Users.
M-N	For single-user software, or that used with difficulty on networks.
X	User's home directory.
Y	DOS relative to the workstation: PUBLIC/%MACHINES/%OS/%OS_VERSION.
Z	SYS:PUBLIC.

Privileges

Just to recap, as a supervisor, you can do anything. However, other people may need to use commands that are outside their normal terms of reference, so you grant them *privileges*, or *rights of access*, which allow them to get to areas of the hard disk they would not normally be able to, and/or do things to files once they get there (they would usually have their own directory to which they have full rights).

Access privileges comprise much of system security and must be granted to each user for each directory that needs to be accessed by them, which filter down to each subdirectory unless redefined at that level (they do not move horizontally). Privileges can also be granted to groups, whose rights are automatically granted to each member. Directory rights are determined by *trustee assignments*, which are administered by a program called SYSCON, which is described later.

Here they are:

Read	You can read all files in a particular directory, or a single file. In the latter case, you don't need Read privileges for the directory the file is in.
Create	You can create directories.
Write	You can write to files.
Erase	You can delete directories or files.
Modify	You can change the attributes of directories or files, or rename them.
File Scan	You can see filenames when viewing the contents of a directory.
Access Control	You can modify file trustee assignments, which means that you can grant rights to other users (except at Supervisory level, where you have to be a Supervisor).
Supervisory	You can grant all rights and enable any user with this right to do the same for users and groups with files or directories they are responsible for.

Security equivalences

To save you time and overworking the brain, you could grant a *security equivalence* to a user. Equivalences only apply to rights *actually* assigned (as opposed to *equivalently* assigned); for example, Fred is equivalent to Sue, but Tom's equivalence to Sue (the actual user) does not include equivalence to Fred.

Supervisors have all rights in all directories.

Attributes (Flags)

Files and directories can be given special properties, or attributes (flags), that control the way they are used. For example, you can prevent a file from being deleted or copied by anybody, regardless of what access rights they may have. All access privileges are overridden by file attributes.

In all file operations, the ability to open a file is assumed, whatever the subsequent action (that is, you've got to open a file before you can read from or write to it). The attributes include:

Archive needed (A)   This is assigned automatically to files modified since the last backup.

Copy Inhibit (C)   Stops Mac users from copying any file to which this is applied. This overrides the Read and File Scan access privileges, and you need Modify to remove this attribute.

Delete Inhibit (D)   Stops you from erasing directories or files (overrides the Erase right). You need Modify to remove this attribute.

Execute only (X)   Prevents copying or backing up files. Only use it with files that have .COM or .EXE extensions. This attribute cannot be removed, and only supervisors can apply it, so keep a copy of the files affected, just in case. Some applications may not run properly with this.

Hidden (H)   Hides directories and files from sight, and prevents them from being deleted or copied. However, if you have *File Scan* rights, you can see them with the NDIR utility.

Purge (P)   Purges a file immediately it is flagged for deletion.

Read Only/ Read Write (Ro/Rw)   Indicates the ability of a file to be modified. All files are flagged automatically as Read Write upon creation, and thus can be modified at any time, unless Ro is set. Ro automatically activates Delete Inhibit and Rename Inhibit, which thus override access rights. You must have Modify to remove this attribute.

Rename Inhibit (R)   Prevents you from renaming directories or files. You must have Modify to remove it.

Shareable (S)   Allows several people to use a file at the same time; usually used with Ro.

System (Sy)	Hides system files and directories from DIR scans, and stops them from being deleted or copied. If you have File Scan rights, you can see them with NDIR.
Transactional (T)	Activates the *Transactional Tracking System*, or TTS, so that all intended changes are made to the file, or none at all.

Login Scripts

Just as DOS has an AUTOEXEC.BAT file to do the repetitive start-up sequences at the beginning of the day, so NetWare has a *login script*, which is created and edited through **SYSCON**, the administration program.

As with batch files, you can get as complicated as you like, with branches, and conditional commands like IF, THEN, ELSE, etc, but remember it may not be you that has to sort out the mess later! Keep it simple!

There are three types of login script. The *system login script* is operated first (if it exists), then the *user login script*, followed by the *default* if there is nothing else.

In general, it's best to put as many commands as possible in the system login script, and minimise the use of user login scripts, so you don't use up so much disk space (important when you've got a thousand users).

System Login Script

This operates system wide (its effect is global) and is maintained by the supervisor. It is valid for every user and is used each time they log on. You will find it disguised as NET$LOG.DAT in SYS:PUBLIC.

Its contents should map a search drive to the **SYS:PUBLIC** and **SYS:PUBLIC\%MACHINES\%OS\%OS_VERSION** directories (in the case of PC compatibles, this will translate to something like **SYS:PUBLIC\IBM_PC\MSDOS\V3.30**). Your DOS may not be on the fileserver, of course.

Don't forget **COMSPEC = S2:COMMAND.COM**, so that COMMAND.COM reloads properly every time you leave an application.

The sample lines overleaf are a bare minimum, and will ensure that users are able to access the utilities they need and that COMMAND.COM is reloaded properly when they leave a program:

```
MAP INS S1:=SYS:PUBLIC
MAP INS S2:=SYS:PUBLIC/%MACHINE/%OS/%OS_VERSION

COMSPEC=S2:COMMAND.COM
```

If you want to preserve any current drive mappings, use **MAP INS** (MAP INSert), so they are not overwritten.

User Login Scripts

These are text files called **LOGIN** in the relevant user's **\MAIL** directory (e.g **SYS:MAIL\USER_ID**) and are specific to particular people. They override system login script settings, and are also run at login time. Don't use S1, S2 or S3 designations, since that will override the system settings. In other words, start from S4.

The presence of empty ones prevents the use of the default script (rather like the way an empty AUTOEXEC.BAT file will bypass the time and date prompts in DOS).

Default Login Script

Finally, something that is not a login script as such, but a series of commands contained within LOGIN.EXE (in SYS:LOGIN) that act as a default login script if the other two can't be got at for any reason (otherwise it is not normally used). It cannot be edited.

This "default" login script is quite simple, establishing a search drive for PUBLIC and a DOS directory – enough to get you up and running, in other words. However, it does overwrite any PATH instructions from DOS, so the only search drives available to that user would be SYS:PUBLIC and SYS:PUBLIC/DOS.

Commands Used In Login Scripts

MAP	Allocates drive letters to directory paths.
MAP INS	As above, but preserves previous PATH settings.
COMSPEC	Where to find COMMAND.COM.
WRITE	Displays text in quotes on the screen (for messages).
PAUSE	Means what it says.
REMARK	Allows you to make comments within the script for later debugging.

FIRE PHASERS	Makes a Star Wars type noise to catch someone's attention, like with an error message.
#	Used in front of an *external command*, such as CAPTURE. It runs the command, then returns to the login script.
EXIT	Leaves and terminates the login script, which means that if you want to run a program automatically afterwards, you must enclose the command in quotes, so the text will be taken as input to the keyboard buffer.

You can also use normal conditionals (IF...THEN, etc).

Printing

One of the original uses of a LAN was to share expensive equipment like printers, since one user will not use such equipment all the time. Therefore, it's a cost-effective idea to let others utilise any idle time (assuming, of course, that all users have similar demands. A secretary frequently putting out lots of small memos will get very annoyed if the printer is hogged by somebody churning out out 100-page documents).

The suitability of the printer for the application concerned also needs to be thought about (you can't use a daisy wheel with Windows), as well as keeping it supplied on a regular basis with ribbons or paper. The paper issue can get more complicated when you have to mix both headed and plain, or continuous and cut sheet.

Printing from a single PC can be bad enough – on a network it can be a positive headache, once *print queues* are formed. These arise from *spooling*, a process that allows printers to pause for breath occasionally during their work (computers can churn out their data faster than the printers can cope with).

The practical difficulty of this as far as you are concerned is that you cannot see the results immediately – in all probability you will either have to go to the print room or wait for somebody to bring it to you.

The word SPOOL comes from *Simultaneous Peripheral Operation On-Line*, an operation that is supposed to give the impression of doing two things at once. The computer's output is fed to disk instead of the printer and placed in an orderly queue, where the jobs are processed in order of priorities previously set by you.

In this way, programs that process files as they print (rather than just sending them and forgetting them) are fooled into thinking that the job has been completed and are thus ready for something else.

Even a small office will generate long queues, so each print job is normally separated by a sheet with the user's name on it. This is called either a *banner* or a *separator page*, and you should go through a process called *despooling* if you don't want to print something you've already sent on its way, otherwise you'll confuse the printer (i.e. opening up the print queue and deleting it, with PCONSOLE).

You will need to understand how each application you propose to use carries out its printing tasks, and whether the printer needs special setup codes. A common problem is that some programs do not send an end-of-file character at the end of printing, which means the inconvenience of having to leave the program before the print job is accepted. One solution here is to specify a 5-10 second timeout (usually as an option with CAPTURE), telling it to insert the required character if nothing is forthcoming from the computer (watch out for programs that take some time to assemble graphic images, however).

As many programs expect to send their output directly to LPT1 (or whatever), there needs to be some method of redirecting it to a queue. The relevant command is CAPTURE, mostly issued from a login script (preceded with #) so it is active all the time.

Multi-user versions of many packages know about all these problems, including whether to send a banner page or not, and may be able to bypass queues. They also allow users to have private dictionaries and formatting defaults.

NetWare itself can accept a printer in one of several ways. It can be a local printer to a PC compatible workstation or a Mac, or it can be a shared printer hooked to a fileserver or to the LocalTalk part of an AppleTalk network. Each has its own advantages and disadvantages.

A local printer is attached to a workstation, so the printer serves only that workstation unless special utilities (e.g. RPRINTER) are used. This makes sense if the printer is either meant for a specific application, is kept busy or needs a lot of attention while it works (some plotters don't have automatic paper feed, or need continuous two-way communication with the application).

NetWare for Macintosh allows PCs and Macs to share printers, but there are limitations regarding the placement of printers for easy access, especially Postscript compatible ones.

PC printers tend not to say too much to their controlling computers, apart from necessary handshaking signals, whereas the Mac expects continual interaction from a LaserWriter (the printer is actually on the network as a device in its own right).

Shared PC printers are attached to the fileserver, up to five attached to either serial or parallel ports. To access a shared printer from NetWare, use the SPOOL or CAPTURE command, depending on your version of NetWare.

Setting Up A Print Server

Run PCONSOLE, go into *Print Queue Information*, and you'll see a list of print queues. Press **< Insert >**. Type in the name of the new queue, and press **< Return >**. Don't use the default queues (with names like PRINTQ_0), because the underscores may cause problems. Repeat until all the queue names are on the list.

From the main menu, select *Print Server Information*. Press the **< Insert >** key and type a name.

Select *Printer Configuration*. Pick one of the 16 "Not Installed" selections (the most printers that can be managed). Remember the number if you intend to run a remote printer from a workstation; you may need it later for RPRINTER. Press **< Return >** on the printer number.

Use a name that best describes the printer's use (it's only used for menus and status screens). With regard to printer type, if connected to the machine running PSERVER, use *Local*. Otherwise, select *Remote*. Accept the defaults for all the settings.

Go back to the *Print Server Information* menu and select *Queues Serviced By Printer*.

Select the printer from the list, then press the **< Insert >** key to link a queue to the printer. Accept the default priority. Repeat this for each printer connected to the print server machine, and each remote printer it will manage.

Once the server is running, type LOAD PSERVER PRINTER at the : prompt. (PRINTER is the name of the print server). You will see a status screen with a box for each of the 16 printers, in one of which will be the name you called the printer, together with its status.

With NetWare 286, copy PSERVER.VAP from SYS:PUBLIC to SYS:SYSTEM. Down the server and restart it. At some stage you will see: *"Value Added Processes have been defined. Start them?"* Say *Yes*, after which you will be prompted for the name of the print server.

From a workstation, just type PSERVER PRINTER (you can start the print server without logging in if you copy the files to the workstation). Note that you must add the line SPX = 60 to SHELL.CFG.

Remote Printing

Run RPRINTER on the workstations that have printers attached. Copy RPR*.* to SYS:LOGIN, which will enable you to run RPRINTER without logging in.

Add the following lines to AUTOEXEC.BAT (after IPX, etc):

```
RPRINTER PRINTER 1 -r
RPRINTER RPRINTER 1
```

The first line disconnects the remote printer, just in case a workstation has been rebooted. Again, add the line SPX = 50 to the SHELL.CFG file.

Backing Up

Whether (and when) you back up depends on the value of your data and the time and trouble involved in recreating your system. Some companies keep applications on the server and data on workstation hard disks, so if the server goes down for any reason, all that's needed is to recreate the directory structure on its hard disk.

Normally, though, applications and data reside on the server, and a convenient method is required to backup the contents. People in charge of backups must have the proper rights to do so; it's possible to grant extra rights to someone purely for setting up the tape system.

Timing is important. If your company continually works late, then the best time to back up is probably early in the morning. You may find it best to apply NetWare's logging in time restrictions to ensure that nobody is on the system when backing up is in process, as open files are left alone.

NetWare has its own backup software, called NBACKUP, which will use workstation hard disks or tape streamers, if it finds them. However, it 's not sophisticated, and you continually have to enter fresh answers to the questions it asks, which is both inconvenient and hard to work out for inexperienced people.

There are many third party programs that will automate the whole process, and even include workstations by loading memory-resident software at each workstation to talk to the server.

Workstation hard disks can be used to backup file servers. Either use a simple DOS XCOPY /S /E (include subdirectories, even empty ones) command or NetWare's own NBACKUP program.

Tape usage

Make a complete backup daily, with an extra weekly one on the last day. Recycle each tape in its turn, and use another tape for each weekly backup. Make another backup on the last day of the month, and then recycle weekly tapes in addition to the daily ones. Add new monthly tapes to the pile, until the end of the year, when you make an annual backup; recycle all the tapes.

This means that, with only 25 tapes, you will only lose a maximum of a day's work in any week, a week's work in any month and a month's work in a year.

Alternatively, if you have only a basic system, you can do a complete backup at the beginning of the week, and only do the files that have changed on every subsequent day, either on a different tape or appending the new sessions to those on the first tape. The tapes are kept and recycled on a monthly basis. In this case you would only lose a maximum of one day's work within the past four weeks.

You can improve on this if you wish, but bear in mind that tapes do wear out; this is particularly important when putting more than one backup session on a tape.

The Bindery

The Bindery is a database storing data on users and network resources, which sits at the heart of every NetWare fileserver. It consists of three files in the SYS:SYSTEM directory. Two of them, NET$BIND.SYS and NET$BVAL.SYS, are locked and hidden (although they are continuously open), while the third, NET$ACCT.DAT, is updated regularly with accounting data as the network is used.

The information in it includes user names and groups, passwords, server names and how all these items relate to each other. Each object has a unique bindery ID and is categorised by its object type (a directory's trustee list is actually a group of bindery objects).

Objects in the bindery are known as *permanent* when written to the hard disk, and *dynamic* while existing in RAM beforehand.

Bindery files should be backed up frequently, but restoring them needs extra care (you should never overwrite a current version with an old one), and it should only be done when installing or reinstalling a file server or fileserver disk.

Changing File Servers

Upgrades happen all too frequently, and it's not just individual bits. Often it's more convenient to change the whole fileserver. It sounds easy, but it isn't! The main problem is how to save yourself the trouble of typing out all the user details again.

The easiest way is to install NetWare on the new server (off the network) and then connect it up. When you log on from a workstation, it will identify itself (assuming you gave it a different name than the original; if you didn't, NetWare will get VERY upset and beep at you until you change it).

Use NBACKUP to backup the original fileserver on to your workstation, but don't back up data; only select the bindery which, of course, contains all the details of your users and groups, etc. Then restore to the new fileserver, and your system is as it was. You could, of course, include the data in the backup if you wanted to.

Commands And Utilities

Only a selection of the most useful ones are given here. Like DOS, only 20% of commands are used 80% of the time anyway. There are two types, *menu-driven* and *command line*, which are mostly run from workstations, but some command line utilities are used on the server. They are marked with a C in brackets (C). You will find that almost everything revolves around SYSCON, the administration program.

Loadable Modules (VLMs)

These are memory resident programs that lurk in the fileserver.

Utilities

These live in the SYS:PUBLIC directory. Those specific to supervisors are given later.

ATTACH	Access another server while remaining logged in to your curent one (normally, you get logged out automatically).
CAPTURE	Use this to capture data sent to a parallel port and redirect it to network printer queues and files. You can redirect up to three LPT ports, and they don't actually have to exist.

CASTOFF	Stops any messages sent to your workstation from appearing on the bottom line of the screen (otherwise any running programs would stop).
CASTON	Does the opposite, of course.
COMCHECK	Checks communications between servers and workstations.
CONSOLE (C)	When using a non-dedicated fileserver (with 2.x), CONSOLE is used in conjunction with the DOS command to toggle between workstation (DOS) or file server mode. Type DOS to get back to being a workstation. You need to run this before you run the DOWN command.
DOS (C)	See CONSOLE
DOWN (C)	Used to close down the fileserver properly, in that files are closed and the cache contents written to disk before the power is switched off, otherwise they would be lost (with NetWare, data is assembled in RAM before being written to disk). Note, however, that DOWN does not park disk heads.
FILER	A menu-driven file maintenance program. Its major benefit is that it allows you to get rid of complete directory structures without deleting the files in them first. Its two main functions are selection and maintenance; selection, because it's sometimes like looking for a needle in a haystack when searching for files on a hard disk, and maintenance, because you may not want to keep them when you find them anyway.
FLAG	Changes file attributes.
HELP	Gives you quick reference to using other commands.

LOGIN	Allows you to gain access to the fileserver's resources.
LOGOUT	Logs you out of every file server you are logged in to or attached to.
MAP	Allocates drive letters to directory paths.
MENU	This lets you set up a menu system of your own. It uses text files created with an ASCII text editor. Some memory hungry applications might not load if you use this.
MONITOR (C)	A fileserver program that lets you know what your users are doing and how the server is coping with the workload..
NBACKUP	Backs up and restores fileserver contents to and from workstation hard drives and tape streamers. Runs from a workstation.
NCOPY	The same as COPY (in DOS), except that it's used to networks and is faster.
PCONSOLE	Sets up the print server and generally controls network printing.
PRINTCON	Customises print jobs, and is used in conjunction with PRINTDEF (below).
PRINTDEF	Allows full use of a printer's capabilities on a network. It creates a database of device and form definitions (page sizes, for instance) which you can get with NPRINT and PRINTCON. This is how you would tell the system what control codes your printer needs (and when) to get the results you want.
PSERVER	Runs the print server. PSERVER.VLM is for the filserver, PSERVER.EXE is for a workstation and PSERVER.VAP is for a NetWare 2.x fileserver. Only use one at at time.
PURGE	Permanently removes files that have been marked for deletion.

GLOSSARY

Non-italicised explanations to abbreviations are those used on the Internet.

802.3	The official name for Ethernet.
802.4	Official name for a Token passing system on a bus coaxial network.
802.5	The official name for Token-Ring.
802.6	The official name for a Metropolitan Area Network.
802.9	A standard for networking over UTP, supporting voice and data.
10BaseT	Part of 802.3 defining UTP cabling for Ethernet.
AAA	Any Advice Appreciated
AAL	*ATM Adaptation Layer.*
Access	Link up to a computer system or network.
Access Protocol (or Access Method)	The traffic rules that devices on a network abide by when sending signals over the lines (such as CSMA or token passing). Whatever is used, they must ensure that only one station transmits at a time, and if not, that data is not corrupted or lost.
ACCUNET	AT&T Packet Service.
ACD	*Automatic Call Distribution.*

ACF	*Advanced Communication Facility.*
ACK	A non-printing character used to indicate that a block has been received.
Acoustic Coupler	A type of modem that links up to the telephone system through a handset, so it uses sound waves rather than electrical connections for its operations. They are very susceptible to outside noise, as each end of the handset is placed inside a rubber cup for it to work. Its main advantage is portability, and use where there is no phone socket.
ACU	*Automatic Calling Unit.*
Adaptive Routing	As opposed to *alternative routing*, where a network management system keeps track of the state of traffic on every line and decides at the time of transmission which route should be used.
ADC	*Analog-to-Digital Converter.*
ADCCP	*Advanced Data Communication Control Protocol.*
Address	The identifying characters for a network terminal; a pattern of characters identifying a unique storage location, or part of a data block which identifies its destination.
ADGR	All Donations Gratefully Received.
ADP	*Automated Data Processing.*
ADPCM	*Adaptive Delta Pulse Code Modulation.*
AFAIAA	As Far As I Am Aware.
AFAICR	As Far As I Can Recall.
AFAICS	As Far As I Can See.
AFAICT	As Far As I Can Tell.
AFAIK	As Far As I Know.

AFAIR   As Far As I Recall.

AFAIUI   As Far As I Understand It.

AFOAL   A Hell of a Lot.

AFP   *AppleTalk Filing Protocol*. Apple's network file access protocol, similar to NetWare's Core protocols.

AGAN   As Good As New.

AIUI   As I Understand It.

Alias   On a Bulletin Board, an assumed name under which you may post messages.

Alphanumeric   A set of symbols consisting of alphabetic characters, numbers and others.

ALOHA   A method of satellite communications, first used for Hawaii-to-USA connections.

Alternative Routing   A system where information which normally follows one route between two nodes is made to take another if any part of the network is overloaded.

AMEOL   *A Most Excellent Off Line* reader (used with CIX).

Analogue Signal   A continuously variable signal, such as sound. The variations in the signal directly correspond to the information that the signal contains; for example, a louder sound is represented by a higher voltage. In other words, it is *analogous* to it, hence the name.

As the information is directly dependent on the signal, any change in the signal will change the information contained, so analogue signals are very susceptible to noise.

Analogue transmission is used on the telephone system and is not compatible with computer signals (see also *Digital Signals*).

ANI	*Automatic Number Identification*; a feature of telephone systems that passes a caller's number over the system to the receiver so the caller can be identified.
ANSI	*American National Standards Institute.* Defined standard for displaying very low level graphics on PCs. The ANSI standard is used on most Bulletin Boards.
Answer Mode	Used when a modem is set up to receive calls from an originating modem. Hosts are usually in answer mode.
Answer Modem	One which accepts a call from an originating modem.
Answer Tone	The tone (defined by V.25) given out by a modem before the carrier to indicate to the caller that a modem has answered.
API	*Applications Programming Interface.* Defines the way in which programmers should create their products so they can interact with others.
APPC	*Advanced Program-to-Program Communications.* This is an IBM protocol analogous to the Session Layer in the OSI Model. It enables data to be sent around a network.
APPN	*Advanced Peer-to-Peer Networking.*
Appleshare	Apple Computer's network product, which requires a dedicated Macintosh as a server. It includes both server and workstation software and uses AppleTalk Filing Protocols (see next). Macintosh II servers can support up to 50 workstations, while a Plus or SE is limited to 32.
Appletalk	A set of communications protocols used to define networking on an AppleShare network. It is based on OSI.
Application Layer	The highest level of the OSI Model which describes the way that programs interact.

Application Software	Programs designed for a specific task, such as wordprocessing.
Archiver	A file compression utility, such as PKZIP, PKXARC or ARJ. On a Bulletin Board, large files can be compressed with this program to a fraction of their formar size, either to reduce the time on line or to save disk space.
ARCNET	*Attached Resources Computing.* A networking architecture based on a bus topology and which uses token passing as a basis of its operations.
ARPA	*Advanced Research Projects Agency.*
ARQ	*Automatic Request Repeat.* A method of error checking, sometimes used as a synonym for MNP.
ASAP	As Soon As Possible.
ASCII	Acronym for *American Standard Code for Information Interchange* (pronounced "ask-ee"). A standard code where characters are given numbers. Sometimes used as a synonym for "plain text".
ASCII File	A file containing only ASCII characters.
Asymmetrical Duplex Transmission	Transmission which takes place in both directions at the same time, but not at the same speed, e.g. 1200/75 bps. Sometimes known as Pseudo Full Duplex.
Asynchronous	A type of communication distinguished by the lack of a set timing arrangement (sometimes called "start-stop"). Extra signals are transmitted to inform the receiving device when a complete character begins and ends (start and stop bits). Thus, the meaning of a bit is dependent on its position in relation to the start and stop bits rather than its correspondence with the computer's clock.

Asynchronous Transfer Mode	See ATM.
AT Command Set	An industry standard group of modem commands, each of which must be preceded by the letters AT in order to get the modem's attention (as used by Hayes). For instance ATDP012265764 tells the modem to dial (D) with pulses (P) the following number.
ATM	At The Moment/*Adobe Type Manager/Automated Teller Machine/Asynchronous Transfer Mode*.
	Asynchronous Transfer Mode is a high speed method of packet switching that uses fixed length packets at speeds of up to 155 megabits/second. Also known as *cell relay*; ATM "cells" are 53 bytes in size, 5 for the address and 48 for the information.
Attenuation	The difference between transmission and reception due to losses through equipment, lines or other devices, or signal loss over distance.
AUI	*Attachment Unit Interface*. A 15-pin socket used for Thick Ethernet connections found on the NIC.
Auto Answer	The ability for a modem to automatically answer the telephone when it rings. It detects the incoming ringing voltage and siezes the line, whereupon it sends a signal to its host computer to let it know what's going on. This enables systems to be left running without attention.
Autodial	Describes a modem capable of automatic initiation of calls, without the use of a handset, as in *Autodial Modem*.
Automatic Number Identification	See ANI.

Automatic Repeat reQuest (ARQ)	A method of error correction where the receiving terminal automatically requests a block of data to be resent if any errors have been detected in the original transmission.
Automatic Send and receive (ASR)	A system which enables incoming messages to be stored and outgoing messages to be sent.
Auto-partitioning	A condition where a hub detects that a device connected to one of its ports has been involved in more than 30 consecutive collisions, or the port is automatically disabled or partioned, and frames will not be passed through it.
Auto Recall	A facility on some autodial modems which enables them to redial an engaged number repeatedly until it is available.
AVHBI	A Very Happy Bunny Indeed!
BABT	*British Approvals Board for Telecommunications.* An offshoot of the Department of Trade and Industry which ensures that equipment attached to the telephone system does not ruin the system by making everything that is to be attached pass through a rigorous testing procedure. Approval is signified by a white label that contains a green circle.
Backbone	A high speed, high capacity link between individual networks in a large organisation. It will usually use Thick Ethernet or Fibreoptic cable.
Background	In time-sharing or multi-tasking, the lowest priority work the computer will perform when other work is to be done, or work done at the same time as a main task that is subordinate to it. Some programs have the ability to communicate in the background; i.e. get on with downloading a file while awaiting user input during text editing or other functions.

Backplane	The bus which links individual networks in a hub.
Backup	A duplicate copy of a program or data. A spare system available if the main one goes down.
Backward Channel	A supervisory channel, not used as a main channel of communication.
Bandwidth	The range of frequencies that a circuit can reliably carry or, more properly, the difference between the highest and lowest possible frequencies that are available for signalling on a given channel.
Base Address	The first address in a series in memory, describing an expansion card's I/O space.
Baseband	Where an unmodulated signal carries information, using the entire frequency range of the medium, as used in most Local Area Networks.
	Data is transmitted in its raw state, not being modulated in any way. Only one signal at a time can travel along the cable.
	Although potentially fast, the effective speed of baseband systems may be slower than the official rating. With only one channel available, you can't retransmit on another one if there's a bottleneck, but have to wait till there's a gap.
Baseband Coax	A single channel medium for carrying baseband transmissions.
Basic Rate Interface	See BRI.
Batch	A collection of similar work which can be processed in one operation.
Batch Mode	Running a program without user interaction. In networking or mainframes, this refers to batch transfers where an entire file is downloaded from a central machine, worked on and returned (e.g. file transfer).

Baudot Code   A 5-bit data code used in telegraphy, telex and RTTY. The code is named after J M E Baudot, a French telegraphy expert, whose name is also remembered in....

Baud Rate   A measurement of the rate of signal changes per second when communication takes place between separate devices. When used with reference to printers and similar devices, it is normally equal to bits-per-second, so the two terms can be used in place of each other as one bit is generally transmitted per signal change. However, with modems, it's not strictly correct above a certain speed, say 1200 baud, as the number of bits transmitted per second will not exactly equal signal changes because more bits are squeezed on to the tone. However, the terms are still used loosely in place of each other.

Dividing the Baud rate by 10 gives the approximate number of characters transmitted per second. Both transmitter and sender need to have the same Baud rate to communicate successfully.

BBDC   Big Boys Don't Cry.

BBS   See *Bulletin Board*.

BCNU   Be Seeing You.

Bell   Standards used for communications over the USA telephone system. For instance, where the UK would use CCITT standard V.21 to denote 300 baud operation, Americans would use Bell Standard 103.

BERT   *Bit Error Rate Test*(er).

BFN   Bye For Now.

BGI   Bloody Good Idea.

BHOW   Bangs Head On Wall.

BIIK   Blowed If I Know.

Binary	The native language of all computers. Numbers, letters, and instructions are represented in 1s and 0s (or Ons and Offs) inside the computer.
Binary File	As opposed to an ASCII file (or any other in a structured form), a file where the data is not in a recognisable pattern but where any bit may be either on or off. Examples are graphic and program files.
Bindery	A NetWare database that keeps track of users and other information.
BIR	*Burst Information Rate.*
B-ISDN	*Broadband ISDN.*
Bisynchronous	An IBM-developed protocol for mainframe computers involving synchronous transmission which is controlled by a clocking signal.
Bit	Contraction for *BI*nary digi*T*. A single 1 or 0 switch and the smallest unit of unambiguous information used in a computer. Patterns of bits represent characters or symbols (see *Byte*).
Bit Rate	The speed at which bits are transmitted, that is, the number of bits that can pass through a communications channel in one second. Not necessarily the same as *Baud Rate* (see above).
Bits per second	Another name for *bit rate*.
Bit Synchronisation	The same as synchronous transmission.
BIU	*Basic Information Unit*, or *Bus Interface Unit*.
Block	A preset number of characters which are transmitted together as a separate unit.
BLU	*Basic Link Unit.*
BMAP	*Bit-Mapped Alphanumeric Processor.*

Boot   Short for "bootstrapping", which means starting the computer up, usually at the beginning of the day's work.

BOB   *Break-Out Box.*

BOC   *Bell Operating Company* (see *Bell*).

BRI   ISDN standard governing how desktop terminals and telephones can connect to the ISDN switch, specifying two 64 Kbps B channels that allow simultaneous voice and data and a D channel for call, and customer information at 16 Kbps.

Bridge   A device that links LANs so that the facilities on each are available to the other, with the side benefit of keeping traffic where it belongs, thus reducing congestion. A bridge can only sense whether a packet belongs on the local network or should be sent on; it has no facility for making routing decisions, as has a router. A bit like a sentry.

Broadband   American for *Wideband*. A communications method that uses a large bandwidth with several channels multiplexed on to it.

                  Broadband networks require special tuning and strict procedures in order to work properly, which implies trained support staff. Typically, stations using specialised modems transmit on one frequency to a translation module (referred to as the head end transmitter) at the end of the cable which amplifies the received signals and shifts them to a second group of frequencies, whereupon they're sent back the way they came (assuming they haven't been picked up by any station on their way there). Thus retransmitting doesn't cause a traffic jam and there's plenty of flexibility.

                  Where two cables are used, each either transmits or receives, so the head end merely provides a passive path between cables.

Broadcast Service   A data service in which all users receive the same information, but only the addressee acts on it (such as with Ethernet).

Brouter   A combination of a bridge and a router, which can route one or more protocols and bridge all others.

BRS   Big Red Switch.

BSA   *Burroughs Synchronous/Asynchronous.*

BSC   *Binary Synchronous Communication.*

BSD   *Berkeley Software Distribution.*

BSF   But Seriously, Folks.

BSRF   *Basic Synchronous Reference Frequency.*

BTAN   *Basic Telecommunication Access Method.*

BTDT   Been There Done That.

BTDTGTTS   Been There Done That Got The T Shirt.

BTLZ   *British Telecom Lempel-Ziv.* Custom version of the compression algorithm incorporated in V.42 bis.

BTU   *Basic Transmission Unit.*

BTW   By The Way.

Buffer   A small amount of memory which temporarily holds data until it can be transmitted or processed by another device. This compensates for the different rates of data flow.

Buffered Repeater   A device that amplifies and regenerates signals so that they can travel further along a cable. The buffer assists in controlling the flow of data.

Bug	A hardware or software error. The word was first coined from early computer days when a singed butterfly was found to have clogged up the works of a computer.
Bulletin Board System (BBS)	A messaging and noticeboard system owned and run by a computer enthusiast, although some commercial organisations and local authorities run them as well. It's sometimes run on a home micro connected to an autoanswer modem, but can be quite sophisticated.
Bus	A path for electrical signals. A linking arrangement that carries data broadcast around a network or inside a computer (such as a data bus or a control bus).
Byte	The basic unit of computer memory, or a collection of bits. In a PC, a byte consists of eight On or Off switches, or bits, which are handled as one unit. Each character or number is represented by one byte.
Cache	A small amount of memory, similar in concept to a buffer, that anticipates data that will be accessed again – as the information needed comes from RAM (as opposed to disk), operations become very speedy.
CAD	*Computer Aided Design.*
CAE	Computer Aided Engineering.
Call Accept	In packet switching, the packet that confirms that the party is willing to proceed with the call.
Call Clearing	The disconnecting of a call.
Call Packet	A packet containing addressing and other information that is needed to establish an X.25 switched virtual circuit.
Call Redirection	In packet-switching, allowing the call to be automatically redirected from the original to another address.

Call Request	In packet switching, the packet sent to initiate a datacall.
Caller ID	See ANI.
CAM	*Computer Assisted Manufacturing.*
CANX	Cancelled
Capacitance	The ability of a non-conductive material to store electricity.
Carrier	The high-pitched, continuous tone you hear on the telephone line that indicates a modem is in operation or, more properly, a continuous frequency signal that can be modified to carry data.
Carrier Detect	A means of sensing when a data call has been answered.
CASE	*Common Application Service Element.*
CCH	*Channel Check Handler.*
CCITT	The initials of the name (in French) of the International Telegraph and Telephone Consultative Committee, now superseded by ITU-T. Representatives of bodies concerned in Telecommunications meet under its auspices to agree standards for International networking of telecommunication services. Famous for the Fax, V and X series of standards.
CCP	*Communication Control Program.*
CDPD	*Cellular Digital Packet Data.* A standard for data communications that uses the unused signal in the bandwidth reserved for cellular voice transmissions.
CDR	*Call Detail Recording.*
CDRM	*Cross-Domain Resource Manager.*
CD-ROM	*Compact Disc Read-Only Memory*

CDRSC	*Cross-Domain Resource.*
CEI	*Comparably Efficient Interconnection.*
Central Processing Unit (CPU)	The main unit of the computer which interprets and executes instructions.
Centralised Network	A network based around a central server which deals with all network tasks.
CEPT	*Conference for European Post and Telephone.*
CGA	*Colour Graphics Adapter*; IBM-PC video display adapter with a resolution of up to 640 x 200.
Channel	A path along which signals carrying data can be sent.
CGI	*Computer Graphics Interface* (ANSI).
Channel Encoding	Data reduction by methods that depend on the properties of the transmission medium.
Character	A single digit, letter, punctuation mark, or other symbol which the user can read or write. In most microcomputers or word processors, one character is stored or expressed in one byte.
Character Mode Terminal	One which communicates asynchronously. In packet switching, one which can only access via a PAD.
Check Bit	The same as the parity bit.
CICS	*Customer Information Control System.*
CIM	*Computer Integrated Manufacturing.* Industrial workflow automation.
Circuit	Like a channel, a path along which data-carrying signals are sent, but implying two-way communication.

CIR	*Committed Information Rate*, or the transport speed a frame relay network will maintain between service locations.
Circuit Switching	A situation where communication takes place along a circuit established for the duration of the call, as used by the telephone system. Once the call has finished, the temporary circuit is broken up into its constituent parts.
CIS	*Compuserve Information Service.*
CIX	*Compulink Information eXchange.* Conferencing system (or multi-user Bulletin Board). European rival of Compuserve.
Cladding	The outer layer of transparent material in an optical fibre, the refractive index of which is lower than the core so the light can bounce further along the fibre.
Clear Packet	On an X.25 circuit, performs the equivalent of hanging up the phone.
CLI	*Command Line Interface.*
Client	A workstation on a network, as opposed to a stand-alone PC which is a high performance graphics workstation. Sometimes known as a *Requester.*
Client/Server	Refers to a network in which several PCs (clients) are connected to one or more servers. With regard to databases (on a network), it's where the database runs on the server as well as the client, where it normally would all be. This arrangement is used to save traffic over the wires.
CMOS	*Complementary Metallic Oxide Semiconductor.* A method of chip manufacture.
Closed User Group	An area within a computer system which is only available to certain subscribers, such as the local river-widener's club on Prestel.

Cluster	When two or more terminals are connected to a data channel at a single point.
COBOL	*Common Business-Oriented Language.* A high-level computer language
CODEC	*Coder/Decoder* and analogue-to-digital converter
Collision Domain	A segment or more joined by repeaters.
Concentrator	See *Hub*.
Coaxial Cable	Cable with two conductors (copper), one inside the other, both sharing the same axis. The central conductor carries the signal while the outer one has the dual function of providing the ground return path and the screen against interference.
Collision Sense Multiple Access	A contention method of avoiding conflict between network stations. Each station transmits at will until a collision occurs between the two sets of transmitted data. The two stations back off for a random interval, then retransmit.
Common Carrier	A telecommunications resource providing facilities to the public (more to do with the USA where private companies run the telephone system).
Compuserve	*Compuserve Information Service* (CIS). On-line data service based in USA, with UK phone numbers for easy access. Sometimes known as CI$, or Compu$pend.
Congestion	The condition of a communications system which is beyond the traffic limits it can handle properly.
Connect Time	The length of time connected to a remote computer, often used as the measure of payment.

Contention	Competition between parts of a system for use of a common resource, such as between terminals for a network path.
Control Character	A Character in an alphabet used for functional purposes rather than signifying text. For instance, it may be used to cause a particular procedure to be started, finished or changed.
Core	The inside cable of an optical fibre.
COS	*Corporation for Open Systems.*
CPE	*Customer Premise Equipment.*
CP/M	*Control Program [for] Microcomputers*, Digital Research Inc's pre-DOS operating system.
CPS	*Characters per second.*
CPU	*Central Processor Unit.*
CRC	*Cyclic Redundancy Check.*
Crosstalk	Not what you get from the Bank Manager, but interference created when magnetic fields interrupt electrical currents, commonly from one cable to another. Eliminated by shielding and/or twisting one wire round another.
Crossover Cable	One where transmit and receive data pairs are crossed over, so that the transmit from one machine is the input to another.
CRT	*Cathode Ray Tube*; used to mean a terminal, monitor, or display using a TV-like tube for primary output
CSMA	*Collision Sense Multiple Access* (or the *Civil Service Motoring Association*). The method used on Ethernet to see if other systems are transmitting before sending.
CSU	*Channel Service Unit.*

CTS	*Clear To Send.*
CUL	See You Later.
CUM	*CIX User Manual.*
Cyclic Redundancy Check	An error detection method.
DARPA	*Defense Advanced Research Projects Agency.*
Data	Information expressed in a formalised way (usually digital) for processing by computers.
Database	A collection of data used as an information source.
Data Compression	Reducing the volume of data for transmission purposes, in order to reduce the time on line.
Data Bit Length	The number of bits carrying the actual character within a byte. The data bit length can be set to 5, 6, 7 or 8. Most services use either 7 or 8 data bits.
Data Circuit-terminating Equipment (DCE)	Equipment, such as a modem, used for passing information to a terminal. It can establish, maintain and terminate a connection and provides the signal conversion required for communication between Data Terminal Equipment and the telephone line.
Dataline	In packet switching, a dedicated line between a customer's terminal and a Packet Switching Exchange (PSE).
Data Link Layer	The second layer of the OSI model where protocols manage the flow of data between the stations so that it arrives safely.
Data Network	A digital communications network with the ability to provide multiple access paths between users.

Data Network Identity Code (DNIC)	Part of the user address on the Packet Switch Stream which identifies the country and type of service.
Data Packet	Transports full-duplex information on an X.25 switched or permanent virtual circuit. May contain up to 1024 bytes of data, but more commonly 128 bytes (default).
Data Set	American for modem, used in the same sense as "radio set".
Data Terminal Equipment (DTE)	The equipment which acts as a terminal on a computer system or network.
DBMS	*Data Base Management System.*
DBX	*Digital Branch Exchange.*
DCD	*Data Carrier Detect.*
DCE	See *Data Circuit-terminating Equipment.* Not to be confused with *Distributed Communication Environment.*
DCS	*Digital Cross-connect System.*
DDE	*Dynamic Data Exchange.*
DDS	*Dataphone Digital Service.*
DEC	*Digital Equipment Corporation.*
Dedicated	Reserved for a single function or user, as in *dedicated file server* or *dedicated line.*
Default Value	A definition that is selected when nothing else is specified.
Demand Multiplexing	A form of multiplexing in which the allocation of time to devices requiring to transmit is made according to whether they actually have data to send or not. That is, no time slot is given if there is no data to send.
Demodulation	The opposite of modulation — reconstituting data after it has been modulated.

DGUTDJ	Don't Give Up The Day Job.
Diagnostics	Programs or routines that test hardware and software.
Dial-up	The use of a dial to initiate connections on switched networks, such as using the PSTN as opposed to a leased line.
Dial-up System	A system which has its own line and an auto-answer modem. Callers will be allowed access to the system automatically.
Digital Service Unit	See *DSU*.
Digital Signal	A type of signal in which information is coded as a series of pulses or signal transitions; for example, those in a computer that are coded in combinations of 0s and 1s to represent data. They are used in a computer because they can assume one of two states, usually a high or low voltage, that will correspond to the on or off states of the binary system used in the computer.
	Because it's the pattern and not the strength of the signal that conveys the message, digital signals are relatively immune to noise compared to analogue ones.
DIN	*Deutsche Industries Norm*; German equivalent of British Standards
DIN Connector	Electrical connector meeting DIN specifications
DIP	*Dual In-Line Package*.
Direct Connect	Attaching a station to the network without a multiplexer, usually through a Network Interface Card.
Distributed File Systems	These allow one computer on a network to use the files and peripherals of another as if they were locally available.

Distributed Network	Another name for peer-to-peer network, where there is no central server and each workstation takes some of the workload.
DLC	*Data Link Control.*
DLE	*Data Link Escape.*
DMA	*Direct Memory Access.* A high speed method of transferring data directly into the computer's memory without intermediate stages.
DOD	*Department of Defense* (USA).
Domain	A collection of servers and clients controlled by a single server.
Door	A program that allows access to files and programs not built in to a Bulletin Board, and allowing them to be run on-line.
DOS	Acronym for *Disk Operating System.* The programs responsible for housekeeping and communications inside the computer, and between peripheral units.
Downlink	A path from a satellite to a ground station.
Downloading	Transferring data from a host to your computer.
DPMI	A method of allowing DOS programs to use the protected mode of the 386/486.
DPSK	*Differential Phase Shift Keying.*
DQDB	*Distributed Queue Dual Bus.*
DQM	Don't Quote Me.
DQMOT	Don't Quote Me On That/This.
Drive Mappings	The allocation of drive letters to disk drives and/or directories; for example, the drive letter d: on your machine could be allocated to drive c: on another machine in the network.

DS9	Deep Space Nine.
DSR	*Data Set Ready.*
DSU	*Digital (Data) Service Unit* (e.g. a digital modem). A synchronous serial data interface that buffers and controls the flow of data between a network entrance point, such as a bridge or router, and the channel service unit.
DTE	*Data Terminal Equipment.* A device that requires its standard 25- pin RS232 port to be wired in a certain way in order to plug directly into DCE equipment (see above) and work straight away (pin 2 will transmit data and pin 3 will receive it).
	Again, if you wish to connect DTE to DTE you will have to cross some of the wiring in the cable to get the signals where they are expected.
DTD	Drop To DOS.
DTE/DCE addressing	Needed for X.25, when confusion may arise about what to connect to what. A simple way is to remember that T = terminal, and C = Clock, so the DCE provides the timing for the circuit. The X.25 is generally configured as DTE and the modem or Network Terminal Unit (NTU) as the DCE.
DTLOI	Due To Lack Of Interest.
DTR	*Data Terminal Ready.*
DTU	*Digital Terminal Unit.*
Dumb Terminal	One which can only send and receive data. It has no "intelligent" features and thus is unable to store or process it.

Duplex   A method of operating a communications circuit between two devices. Full-duplex allows both units to send and receive simultaneously. Half-duplex allows only one unit to send information at one time, although the link may be capable of two-way transmission.

Duplexing   The use of duplicated system components in a backup system.

DWIM   Do What I Mean.

DWIS   Do What I Say.

Earth Station   A station which can transmit and/or receive radio signals to or from a communications satellite.

EBCDIC   *Extended Binary Coded Decimal Interchange Code.* IBM's alternative to ASCII.

Echo   An effect on long communications lines caused by successive amplifications of the signal. Echo-suppressors can be used to combat this. Can also mean the duplication on screen of characters sent along the wire.

Echoplex   One way of checking accuracy by echoing back the information that was sent and displaying it on the originating terminal's screen — if it isn't the same as what was sent, then it's re-transmitted.

Not to be confused with Half-Duplex.

EIA   *Electronic Industries Association.*

Electronic Mail   A system where people can send and receive messages between themselves.

Emulation   How one device mimics another. Not the same as simulation, which does not take place in real time.

Encryption	Encoding messages in order to make them unreadable; PCs can do this very well by themselves, you might say, but this is for security purposes so that only the intended recipient can read them.
EOT	*End of Transmission.*
Error Checking Protocol	A scheme designed to detect errors in blocks of data transmitted through digital systems.

Each block is made up of a number of bytes (not necessarily a whole message) which are summed and an extra byte representing the value of the sum is transmitted along with it. The process is repeated at the other end and the results compared. If they are the same, then no error is assumed. The more rigorous the checking, the slower the whole operation, and the same protocol must be used at each end.

There are many protocols, from Xmodem (the original) to MNP (Microcom Network Protocol) or Kermit. |
ESF	*Extended Superframe Format.*
Ethertalk	Appletalk packets encapsulated so that they can run on Ethernet cables.
Equalisation	A method of compensation for distortion over long communications channels.
Escape Code	A character which changes the meaning of the characters which follow it. It is usually used to add graphics characters or screen positioning commands.
Ethernet	A network cable and access protocol scheme, using baseband coax in a bus topology with a 10 Mbps data transfer rate.
ETX	*End of Transmission.*
Exchange	A switching point in a telephone or telegraph network.

Facsimile Transmission	A system for transmitting documents in binary format over the telephone lines.
FAQ	*Frequently Asked Question.* There are lists of these almost anywhere on the Internet, which you're meant to download straight away and read before you start, to save you clogging the system with useless traffic. The main source is rtfm.mit.edu.
FAX	Short for *Facsimile Transmission*.
FCS	*Frame Check Sequence* (CRC or check-sum).
FDDI	*Fibre Distributed Data Interface.* A stand-ard for using fibreoptic cables in a ring configuration at 100 Mbps. Uses hubs. Not everything will necessarily conform to it.
FDL	*Facility Data Link.*
FDM	*Frequency Division Multiplexing.*
FDX	*Full duplex.*
FEIYD	For Ever In Your Debt.
FGS	For God's Sake.
Fibreoptics	A data transmission method that uses light pulses sent over glass cables to represent data.
FIFO	*First In First Out.*
File Lock	See *Locking*.
File Server	A computer dedicated to managing the files for a network. Sometimes it can't be used for anything else, and Murphy's Law dictates that it will be the best machine available (it may need to be high perfor-mance and is typically based on an 80286 or 80386 processor). See also *Server*.
FILO	*First In Last Out.*

FITMR	Fixed In The Maintenance Release (Oh Yeah?)
FITNR	Fixed In The Next Release.
Flag	In HDLC, the special sequence of 8 bits (01111110) used to determine the opening and closing of a frame.
Flow Control	The control of data flow between systems to prevent overspilling of queues or buffers, or loss of data because the intended destination is unable to accept it. Typically, the use of Ctrl-S (XON) will pause everything and Ctrl-Q (XOFF) will restart it.
FOAF	Friend Of A Friend.
FOC	Free Of Charge.
FOCL	Falls Off Chair Laughing.
Footprint	The area of the Earth in effective line-of-sight communication with a satellite, or within a satellite's transmission area.
Foreground	The area where computer program(s) in a multi-tasking or time-sharing environment have a higher priority than other functions operating at the same time. A station may be operating a wordprocessor in the foreground while network operations may be carried out in the background.
FOTP	Fresh Off The Press.
FOTS	For Old Times Sake.
Four Wire Circuit	A circuit consisting of a combination of two standard pairs of cable, used for speech.
FPPL	*Full Period Private Line.*

Frame	In Time Division Multiplexing, a frame is one complete cycle of events. It will usually consist of a sequence of time slots with extra bits for framing, alarms and so forth.
	The word is also used for a group of data bits, with a flag at each end to indicate its beginning and ending, and on videotext systems to describe one screenful of information, and is always a predetermined number of characters, e.g. 716 on Prestel.
Frame Bandwidth Allocation	The sum of the CIRs associated with all the permanent virual circuits (notional leased lines, in other words) for a customer.
Frame Relay	A simplified form of X.25 packet switching that is faster because it uses less overheads, such as error checking, which is left to the equipment at each end of the line.
Framing	The method by which individual frames are recognised so that slots can be identified correctly.
Frequency Division Multiplexing	A form of multiplexing for analogue signals which allows more than one signal to be transmitted on one channel by using different frequencies.
Front End Processor	A computer acting as an interface between the main computer system and a network. It looks after all the communications and does not take part in any of the data processing.
FSK	*Frequency Shift Keying.* A simple modulation method used by slow modems. it works by varying the frequency of a carrier tone.
FTAM	*File Transfer, Access and Management* protocol.
FTP	*File Transfer Protocol.*
FTR	For The Record.
FU	Fouled Up.

FUBAR	Fouled Up Beyond All Recognition.
FUD	Fear, Uncertainty And Doubt.
Full Duplex	Simultaneous transmission of data in two directions at the same time.
FWIR	From What I Recall.
FWIW	For What It's Worth.
FX	Effects (e.g. stage directions!).
FY	Faithfully Yours.
FYI	For Your Information.
Gateway	The junction between two networks, which may look to each network like one of its own nodes, as the gateway emulates the required software at each end. Used typically between a Local Area Network and a Wide Area Network, or a mainframe with different protocols. A good example is linking a LAN to an X.25 system through an X.25 gateway.
GBS	Get Better Soon.
GFI	Go For It.
GHz	*GigaHertz.*
GOSIP	*Government OSI Profile.* A standard laid down by the government (the word "standard" is used loosely here, as all GOSIPs aren't the same).
GPF	*General Protection Fault.*
GR&D	Grinning, Running & Ducking.
GTBOS	Glad To Be Of Service.
GUI	*Graphical User interface.*
GWS	Get Well Soon.

H.261	ITU-T standard for video compression, allowing video over basic 64 k/bps ISDN.
Half Duplex	The use of a circuit in only one direction at a time, although the circuit may be capable of transmission in two directions at once.
Handshaking	Agreed signals sent between two devices that ensure the process is carried out correctly. Both sides of the interface control the rate of operation.
Hayes Command Set	A standard group of commands relating to autoanswer/autodial modems originally developed by Hayes, but which have now become an industry standard (see also *AT Command Set*).
Hayes Compatibility	The ability of a modem to conform to the standards laid down by Hayes, ranging from just recognising the basic command set to full emulation.
HDLC	A set of protocols defined by ISO for carrying data over a link with eror checking and flow control. Not a "high level" protocol, despite its full name of *High Level Data Link Control*.
HDX	Short for *Half Duplex*.
HEX	Abbreviation for *hexadecimal*.
Header	Extra data attached to transmitted information which contains the identification of the sender and receiver.
Hertz	Cycles per second.
Hexadecimal	A computer character set that uses the Base 16. The numbers 0-9 and the letters A-F express numbers from 0-15 where $A = 10$, $B = 11$ and so on to $F = 15$.
HI	Her Indoors.

High Level Protocol	A protocol which allows network users to carry out functions at a higher level than merely transporting data.
Host Computer	Any computer which serves others connected to it. It may also provide a network service, and is therefore equivalent to a server. The computer behind CIX is a good example.
HTF	How the Hell.
HTH	Hope This Helps.
Hub	A device, placed centrally, that repeats or regenerates signals sent over the network; a form of amplifier, or repeater. Used with 10baseT, Ethernet, FDDI or Arcnet, but increasingly others.
HWISTKT	How Was I Supposed To Know That?
HWSTWH	He Would Say That, Wouldn't He?
Hz	Hertz.
IAC	In Any Case.
IAE	In Any Event.
IAH	In All Honesty.
IANAL	I Am Not A Lawyer.
IBM	Its Being Mended/Its Better Manually/I Believe in Magic.
ICMP	*Internet Control Message Protocol.*
ICYDK	In Case You Didn't Know.
ID	Identity.
IEEE	*Institute of Electrical and Electronic Engineers*, a standard-setting body established in the USA.
IHAG	I'd Hazard A Guess.

IIABDFI	If It Aint Broken, Dont Fix It.
IIDKB	If I Didn't Know Better.
IIR	If I Recall/Remember.
IIRC	If I Recall/Remember Correctly.
IIUC	If I Understand Correctly.
IIUYC	If I Understand You Correctly.
IIWY	If I Were You.
IKWYM	I Know What You Mean
IMail	Abbreviation of Internet Mail, otherwise known as E-Mail.
IMCO	In My Considered Opinion.
IME	In My Estimation/Experience.
IMHA	In My Humble Analysis.
IMHE	In My Humble Estimation/Experience.
IMHO	In My Humble Opinion/In My Honest Opinion.
IMNSHO	In My Not So Humble Opinion.
IMO	In My Opinion.
Impedance	The amount of opposition to an electrical current, which will casue it to weaken. Roughly equivalent to friction.
IMVHO	In My Very Humble Opinion.
Information Superhighway	The idea that every home and office will be connected in some way to a giant network of information providers, consisting of a central backbone of cable running across the country, and tapped by its users.

Input	Data or information which is received into a computer from the outside world. Input may come from disk drives, keyboards, modems, etc.
Intelligent Terminal	As opposed to a Dumb Terminal, one which can actually store and/or process the information received rather than just transfer it.
Interexchange Carrier	See *IXC*.
Interface	The hardware boundary between two parts of a computer or parts of a system which allows communication to take place between them and where the signals passing to and fro are strictly defined – for example, printers must be "interfaced" to the computer in order for them to produce hard copy. The word could also mean a plug, circuit board or anything that allows data transfer between two systems.
Internet	A network of computer networks initially set up to carry E-mail between universities, government agencies, the military or large companies; look on it as a collection of integrated information resources.
	It grew out of the ARPAnet, sponsored by the Defense Department in the US through its Advanced Research Projects Agency, when it just linked four Universities in California to the University of Utah. When the ARPAnet was connected to the CSnet (Computer Science Research Network) it really got going, however, and now links America's major computing centres to the rest of the world.
	The Internet can be used to send E-mail to several on-line services, such as CIX, Compuserve, America On-Line and many Fido-connected BBSs, each of which has its own way of addressing.
Interphobe	Someone with a fear of the Internet.

Interprocess Communication	A facility that gives two programs the ability to share information. Said to be *Local* if they are running on the same machine and *Remote* if otherwise.
Interrupt	A signal that breaks into the execution of a program with a new command.
INTSAT	I'm Not Totally Sure About This.
I/O	Abbreviation for *Input/Output*.
IOTTMCO	Its Obvious To The Most Casual Observer.
IOW	In Other Words.
IP	*Internet Protocol.*
IPX	*Internetwork Packet eXchange.* A NetWare protocol for moving information across a network.
IRMC	I Rest My Case.
IRQ	*Interrupt ReQuest.* A computer instruction that interrupts a running process in order to carry out a task.
ISC	I Stand Corrected.
ISDN	*Integrated Services Digital Network.* A digital telephone system that allows the transmission of voice data, fax and video images over the telephone system. One ISDN line provides 2 64K bps channels plus one control channel.
ISO	*International Standards Organisation.* Based in Paris, it developed the Open Systems Interconnection (OSI) model.
ISTM	It Seems To Me.
ISTMT	It Seems to Me That.
ISTR	I Seem To Recall/Remember.
ISWYM	I See What You Mean.

ITNR	In The Next Release.
ITYR	I Think You're Right.
IWBN	It Would Be Nice.
IWBNI	It Would Be Nice If.
IWFM	It Works For Me.
IWHAGT	I Would Hazard A Guess That.
IWW	I Wonder Why.
IXC	*Interexchange Carrier*. A telephone company! One which uses several transmission methods to transport a message, though.
IYDMMA	If You Don't Mind Me Asking.
IYKWIM	If You Know What I Mean.
IYSWIM	If You See What I Mean.
Jabbering	A condition where a device is transmitting a frame longer than its maximum length.
JAFO	Just Another Flamin' Observer (from the film, *Blue Thunder*).
JAM	Just A Minute...
Jamming Signal	A signal generated by a Network Interface Card on Ethernet to signify that a packet collision has taken place.
JANet	*Joint Academic Network*. Network joining together most UK colleges of further education, based around X.25.
JAT	Just A Tick...
JFTR	Just For The Record.
JPEG	*Joint Photographic Expert Group*. An image file format that compresses the image to save space.

JTFM	Just The Facts, Ma'am/Man.
Jumper	A shorting device, usually made of metal with a plastic surround (very small) that slides over metal pins (usually brass) on a circuit board to allow current to flow between them.
K or KB	Abbreviation for *KiloByte* (1,024 bytes).
Kilobyte	1,024 bytes or characters (actually 2 to the 10th power) roughly corresponding to half an A4 page.
LAN	Short for *Local Area Network*.
LAPB	*Link Access Procedures (Balanced)*. The most common protocol used to interface X.25 DTEs with X.25 DCEs. Full Duplex, point-to-point and bit synchronous. The unit of transmission is a frame, which may contain one or more packets.
LATM	*Local ATM* = on-premise ATM.
LDM	*Limited Distance Modem*.
Leased Line	A private telephone line used for data transmission. Generally of a higher specification than dial-up lines, but not cheap.
LEC	*Local Exchange Carrier*. A local telephone company; i.e. one that only uses one method of transmission.
LGM	Little Green Men.
LIFO	Last In First Out.
LILO	Last In Last Out.
Line	A physical connection between two devices or points.
Linefeed	The command which moves the paper in a printer up by one line, or which on a display screen has the effect of moving the cursor down to the next line.

Link	A circuit or transmission path between a sender and a receiver.
Link Beat	A signal which informs a 10BaseT hub of a device connected to it, and of the link integrity. If the link beat signal is not received at a port, the hub will not transmit packets out of it, even if a cable is attached.
LLC	*Logical Link Control.*
LMI	*Local Management Interface.* A specification for frame relay products that defines a method of exchanging status information between devices.
Local Area Network	A network which provides communication between terminals in a defined area, typically in a building or a floor in that building.
Local Loop	A connection between a customer and the telephone exchange.
Local Mode	Where computers carry out localised processing; not connected to a host system.
LocalTalk	Shielded twisted pair cable used by Apple, formerly called AppleTalk Personal Network Cable.
Locking	A method of protecting shared data. When a file is opened, file locking either prevents simultaneous access by a second program or limits any access to a status such as "read only". DOS versions 3 and later allow an application to lock a range of bytes in a file for various purposes. Where some programs interpret a range of bytes as a record (i.e. databases), it's called *record locking*.
Logical	A word used to describe something that is different from its physical description, for instance, physical drive C: on a station may be logical drive M: on another. A better word would perhaps be "notional".

Logoff	The act of leaving a system, usually by typing LOGOFF, BYE, QUIT, EXIT or something similar.
Logon	The act of gaining access to a system, which may involve using an ID and password.
Logical Channel	The term used to describe each complete transmission in a multiplexed system. "Logical" means "pretend" or "apparent" in this context as, to the user, there seems to be a channel for use, even though there isn't. It's used in the same sense as "virtual", but a better word would probably be "notional".
LOL	Lots Of Luck/Laughing Out Loud.
LSB	*Least Significant Bit*.
LU 6.2	*Logical Unit 6.2* – an IBM protocol for terminals connected to its *System Network Architecture* (SNA). LUs are intended to be the interface between the product and the end user (which may be a program).
M or Mb	One million bytes (1,048,576). Abbreviation for *MegaByte*.
MAC	*Media Access Control*.
MAN	*Metropolitan Area Network*; one operating over the area of a city, or within 50km, with fibreoptics at 100 Mbps. Nodes are connected over 2 km distances.
MAP	*Manufacturing Automation Protocol*. A token-passing bus LAN designed by General Motors. Also a method of assigning drive letters.
MAU	*Multistation (Media) Access Unit*.
Mark	One of the two conditions on a data comms line, the other being *Space*. *Mark* indicates "idle" and is used as a stop bit.
MDBTYD	My Dad's Bigger Than Your Dad.

MDI	*Multiple Document Interface.*
Media	The cabling or wiring (but it may be radio) used to carry signals, typically twisted pair, coax or fibreoptics.
Media Filter	A device for converting the output of an adapter board to work with another type of wiring, to save laying yet more cable. Typically used with Token Ring.
Megabit	Just over 1 million bits.
Megabyte	Just over 1 million bytes (2 to the 20th power; 1,048,576).
MEGO	My Eyes Glaze Over.
Memory Resident	A feature of a program that allows it, once loaded into memory, to remain there until the power is turned off or the computer is reset.
Menu	A screen display that lists choices available to the user and allowing selection with keystrokes.
Menu-driven	Where all the information necessary for the operation of a program is displayed in a menu.
Message	A block of text or data which needs to be transported as a whole.
Message Switching	A method of operating a communications network where whole messages are moved from node to node.
MFT dialling	*Multi-Frequency Tone Dialling*, where different tones represent digits.
MHOTY	My Hat's Off To You.
MHS	*Message Handling Service*. A Novell standard for connectivity, supporting LAN and WAN E-mail connections in store-and-forward fashion.

Microcomputer	A computer system which is based on a microprocessor.
Micron	1/25,000 of an inch. used to specify the core diameter of fibreoptic cable. If you buy the cable before the equipment, get the 62.5 micron size.
Microprocessor	A computer on a chip; an integrated circuit which contains most of the elements of a computer. Also known as CPUs (Central Processing Units), microprocessors are also found in some printers, disk drives, terminals and a variety of non-computer items. When these chips are used for a single purpose within a device, they are known as *dedicated microprocessors*.
MIME	*Multipurpose Internet Mail Extensions*.
MJU	*Multi Junction Unit*.
MMBTY	My Mum's Bigger Than You.
MMS	My Mother Said.
MNP	*Microcom Networking Protocols*. Proprietary standards for error checking and data compression invented by Microcom (or Tricom in the UK). For example, MNP4 error checking means that no spurious characters should appear on the screen during a session with an On-Line Service. The ITU-T equivalent is V.42. MNP 5 includes data compression on the fly, but this has been superseded by V.42*bis*, which can autodetect compressed files and not expand them again, as MNP 5 is prone to do.
Mode	A method of operation, or a phase of program operation.
Modem	Acronym for **MO**dulator-**DEM**odulator. A device which translates computer signals into pulses that can be transmitted over non-computer lines such as those used by the telephone, and *vice versa*.

Modulation	The process of varying some characteristic of a carrier wave in accordance with the data to be transmitted; converting digital signals to analogue signals.
MPEG	*Motion Picture Experts Group.* Responsible for standards concerning video on computers.
MRDA	Mandy Rice Davies Applies ("Well He Would, Wouldn't He?).
MSB	*Most Significant Bit.*
MS-NET	Microsoft's DOS-based contribution to network operating systems, officially known as *Microsoft Networks*.
MT	Empty.
MTIA	Many Thanks In Anticipation.
Multiple Access	Where multiple users can open the same file at the same time.
Multiplexer	Equipment that takes a number of transmission channels and combines them into a common one.
Multiplexing	The process of transmitting more than one signal over a single line.
Multi-tasking	The ability of a computer to do several jobs at the same time (or concurrently, if you want to be posh).
Multi-user	The ability to have more than one person using the resources of a computer at the same time, but usually used to refer to host-to-terminal operations as distinct from peer-to-peer as found in networks.
MUX	Multiplexer
MYOB	Mind Your Own Business.
NAFAIAC	Not As Far As I Am Concerned.

NAFAIC	Not As Far As I'm Concerned.
NAFAIK	Not As Far As I Know.
NALOPKT	Not A Lot Of People Know That.
NCTE	*Network Circuit Terminating Equipment.*
NDA	*Non Disclosure Agreement.*
NDIS	*Network Driver Interface Specification.* A device driver standard created by Microsoft and 3Com. Similar in concept to ODI.
Negative Acknowledgement (NAK)	A control signal which reports that a data block with errors has been received. It usually triggers retransmission of the block concerned.
NETBEUI	*NetBIOS Extended User Interface.* A Microsoft extension to NETBIOS, as used by Windows for Workgroups, etc.
NETBIOS	*Network Basic Input/Output System.* A layer of programming originally developed by IBM and Sytek that sits between the Network Operating System and the hardware concerned, usually the network card. It can also open communications between workstations at the session level. As it is somewhat of an industry standard in its own right, many third-party manufacturers either emulate NETBIOS or provide their own compatible version. On the other hand, many don't.
Network	A system which provides links between users in different places. It provides interconnectivity between varying types of equipment.
Network Interface Card	A circuit board inside a computer that permits direct connection to a network. The board has some intelligence, sometimes has memory and is used to make up packets for transmission.

Network Layer	The third level of the OSI model which contains the logic and rules that determine the path to be taken by data flowing through a network. Sometimes ignored in smaller systems.
Network User Address (NUA)	A number which identifies each subscriber to a network service (e.g. PSS, where it's a 10-digit number) so they can get the money off you. It also provides a means for others to get in touch with you. In PSS, it's issued to each terminal (not a character terminal, as they use PADs).
Network User Identity (NUI)	An identity code given to subscribers to a network service which enables them to access it.
NFS	*Network File System*. One of many file system protocols that allow computers on a network to use the files and peripherals of another one as if they were available locally. Developed by Sun Microsystems and adopted by other manufacturers.
NFW	No Flamin' Way.
NIAL	Not In Acronyms List.
NIC	Network Interface Card.
NIH	Not Invented Here.
NIMBY	Not In My Back Yard.
NIOED	Not In the Oxford English Dictionary.
NITAL	Not In The Acronym List.
Node	A junction of network lines. Often used loosely to mean a terminal.
Noise	Random signals which disturb transmission on lines and cause errors.
NPD	No Problem, Dude.
NRN	No Reply Necessary.

NTOOT	Nine Times Out Of Ten.
Null Modem Cable	A cable configured to resolve the differences between DCE and DTE equipment when connecting like to like (DCE-DCE or DTE-DTE), since each type expects signals on certain pins. As many of the purposes of the pins are crossed over (e.g. 2 and 3 and some handshaking pins), it's sometimes called a *crossover cable*. There are several types of null modem cable depending on the liberties that may have been taken with the RS232 port by the manufacturers of the equipment you propose to connect.
Octet	The name for a byte in packet switching.
ODI	*Open Datalink Interface*. A device driver standard from Novell allowing you to run multiple protocols over one network card.
OEM	*Original Equipment Manufacturer*.
Off Line	Not connected.
OIC	Oh I See.
OLR	*Off Line Reader*.
OMS	Over My Shoulder.
On Line	Connected.
On Line Service	A service provided by an Electronic Mail service such as CIX or Compuserve that provides facilities for your use.
OOTB	Out Of The Box.
OOTD	One Of These Days.
OOTT	One Of Those Things.

Operating System	Sometimes known as DOS, the collection of programs for operating the computer. Operating systems perform housekeeping tasks such as input/output between the computer and peripherals, and interpreting information from the keyboard.
Optical Fibre	Fine, high quality glass fibre, along which light can be transmitted.
Originate Modem	A modem which is only capable of calling a host system.
OS/2	A 32-bit multi-tasking, general purpose operating system for 80386 based computers.
OSI	*Open Systems Interconnection*, a model developed by ISO describing network communication processes and how hardware and software should interconnect if they are meant to work together in a communications system. There are different standards within each layer.
OTOH	On The Other Hand.
OTT	Over The Top.
Overwrite	To write data where other data is stored already. Overwrites occur in networking where two users attempt to write updates to data which is stored in the same place.
OVSN	Out Very Soon Now.
OWIL	Only When I Laugh.
PABX	*Private Automatic Branch eXchange*. Automatic private telephone switchboard.
Packet	A block of data handled by a packet-switched network in a format which contains a header (including the sending and receiving stations' identifications), error checking information and having a maximum size of data field.

Packet Assembler and Disassembler (PAD)	A device in a packet-switched network which prepares data for transmission by converting from serial to packets, and *vice versa*. Thus, it allows ordinary terminals to connect to a packet-switched system.
Packet Interleaving	A form of multiplexing in which packets from various subchannels are interleaved on the line. X.25 is an example.
Packet Switching	A method of sending data in packets rather than as a continuous stream.
Packet Switching Exchange	A node on a packet-switching network that carries out all the switching operations, such as packet assembly/disassembly, the direction of data and so on.
Packet Terminal	A terminal capable of creating and disassembling packets.
PAD	See *Packet Assembler/Disassembler*.
PAD Profile	See *PSS, NUI, NUA and Pad Profile*.
Page	A block of information in a Viewdata system consisting of 26 frames (labelled A-Z).
PAP	*Printer Access Protocol*, which is Apple-Talk's print sharing protocol.
Parallel	In communications, the method of sending an entire character or word at a time over several wires. Parallel communication (usually between the computer and printers) is generally fast, but due to the possibility of electrical interference, transmission lines are kept short (generally less than 10 feet).
Parity	Used in asynchronous serial communications, a method of error checking at byte-level in which an extra bit is added to the number of bits representing a character to indicate how many binary 1s have been transmitted.

The receiving unit compares the information received against this bit and can obtain a reasonable judgment as to the character's validity. Usually, parity may be *even*, *odd* or *none*, but *mark parity* is set to 1 and *space* to 0.

Password

A means of identifying authorised system users consisting of a word or letters. You will be granted access according to whether your password is recognised.

PBX

Private Branch Exchange.

PCM

Pulse Code Modulation.

PC-NET

IBM's DOS-based network operating system, officially known as the *IBM PC LAN Program*.

Peer-to-Peer Resource Sharing

A software architecture that lets any station on a network double as a server while operating locally.

Peripheral

Disk drives, terminals and printers are peripherals. They are controlled by the computer they are connected to.

Permanent Virtual Circuit

A non-physical (i.e. notional) link established between two terminals on a packet switched network. That is, each terminal sees the data stream as if it were on a leased line, but it isn't. This is as opposed to an *open-pipe link*, which is a real connection.

Phantom Voltage

A voltage differential of five volts between the transmit and receive wire pairs in a Token Ring system, which is enough to activate the relays in a MAU, so if a wire breaks, or shorts, the voltage disappears, the relay opens and the ring carries on.

Physical Layer

The first layer of the OSI model which covers such aspects as cabling.

PITA

Pain In The Neck.

PLP *Packet Level Procedures.* These define protocols for transferring packets between an X.25 DTE and X.25 DCE. A full duplex protocol that supports data sequencing, flow control, accountability, error detection and recovery.

PMFJI Pardon Me For Jumping In.

PMJI Pardon Me Jumping In.

Polling A system of regularly inviting stations on a net to transmit, commonly used with fax machines. In a star network, polling from the centre is used to ensure an orderly flow of data to it.

Port The connection which provides an input or output to a system.

POS *Point Of Sale.*

POV Point Of View.

Presentation Layer The sixth layer of the OSI model which formats data for screen presentation and translates incompatible file formats.

PRA ISDN *Primary Rate Access.*

Prestel Viewdata service combining low level text and graphics.

PRI ISDN *Primary Rate Interface.*

Print Server A computer on a network that makes one or more printers attached to it available to other users.

Protocol Rules for the passing of information back and forth between computers. Protocols allow several different types of machinery to communicate on the same network.

Pseudo Full Duplex	Transmitting at high speed while receiving at a low one. With fast turnaround, it's possible to simulate Full Duplex. Also known as *Asymmetrical*, an example of which is HST, used by some US Robotics modems.
PSK	*Phase Shift Keying*. A modulation method used mainly by V.22 modems.
PSS, NUI, NUA and PAD Profile	These relate to the Packet Switch Stream (PSS) network, which is now part of BT's Global Network Services (GNS). Each service is allocated a *Network User Identity* (NUI) and *Network User Address* (NUA) to enable you to gain access to it. You will be asked to enter the NUI and NUA when you sign on to the service. The *Pad Profile* is a two-character code included within each of them which identifies the terminal type, Teletype being A7.
PSTN	*Public Switched Telephone Network*. The name for the standard telephone system.
PTT	*Post Telephone and Telegraph*.
Pulse Code Modulation (PCM)	Representation of an analogue signal by sampling at a regular rate (typically 8000 times a second) and converting each sample to a binary number.
Pulse Dialling	A method of dialling on older exchnges where electrical pulses are generated and sent down the line, as opposed to tones.
PVC	*Permanent Virtual Circuit*.
QAM	*Quadrature Amplitude Modulation*.
QPSK	*Quadrature Phase Shift Keying*.
Queue	A waiting line where jobs are stored for execution, such as a print queue. Technically, a means of bridging speed gaps between different parts of the computer.

RAMDisk	An area of memory programmed to emulate a disk drive. Very much quicker in operation than a physical drive (about 500%), but data is lost when the power is turned off, unless the device is backed up by battery.
RAUBM	Replies As Usual By Mail.
Read-only	A file designation that permits a user to open a file but not modify it.
Read-Write	A file designation that permits a user to open and/or modify it.
Real-time	Generally used to mean "fast response". Originally a system which accepted signals from one environment and could process and return signals quickly enough to be able to control that environment.
Record Locking	See *Locking*.
Redirector	A software module loaded into every workstation. It captures requests from an application program for file and print sharing resources and routes them to where they should be.
Redundancy Checking	The insertion of data (in addition to the information bits) which is used to check the accuracy of data to be transmitted. See also *Parity*.
Register	A temporary storage unit (i.e. memory) for digital information. Found in modems.
Remote Access	Connecting to a network over the telephone lines, usually from home but can be anywhere. You can either control a PC directly, or join as a node through a PC.
Remote Computer	Any computer or terminal with which a communications link has been established.

Repeater	A device which amplifies or regenerates signals to compensate for losses in the system so they can travel further down the cable.
Requester	See *Client*.
Reset Packet	Clears error conditions on an X.25 Switched or Permanent Virtual Circuit. Does not clear the session.
Response Time	The interval needed before a user request is answered.
Resource Sharing	The ability of computers to share and/or use their facilities around a network.
Restart Packet	Notifies X.25 DTEs that an irrecoverable error exists within the network. These clear all existing Switched Virtual Circuits and resynchronise all existing Permanent Virtual Circuits between an X.25 DTE and X.25 DCE.
RFS	*Remote File Service*. One of the many distributed file system network protocols that allow one computer to use the facilities of others as if they were available locally. It is developed by AT&T and adopted as a part of UNIX V.
RHIA	Rubs Hands In Anticipation.
RO(T)FL	Roll On (The) Floor, Laughing.
ROFLWTSDMF	Rolls On Floor Laughing With Tears Streaming Down My Face.
ROUS	Rodents Of Unusual Size (from the film, *The Princess Bride*).
Router	A device linking two or more networks using similar protocols (usually over a wide area), able to forward messages destined for a particular network. It can make routing decisions based on a packets address, and can send packets to the right links.

RS232C	One list of definitions originally for communicating on telephone lines, but also widely used to connect printers and plotters. Defined by IEEE, the US equivalent of V.24.
RSN	Real Soon Now.
RTFM	Read The Flamin' Manual!
RTS	*Request to Send.*
Run Length Encoding	Used commonly in fax transmission, a system of error checking using a byte count instead of sending a stream of identical bytes.
RXD	*Receive Data.*
SAA	*Systems Application Architecture.* A set of specifications written by IBM doing the same as the ISO model, that is, describing how users and programs join together with the intention of unifying its system architecture. This philosophy of common design provides a consistency across the System/370, the System/3x and PS/2. You will find that many (DOS) software menu systems conform to this.
Scrolling	Adjusting the screen display upwards or downwards.
SDLC	*Synchronous Data Link Control.*
Segment	A cable to which devices are connected.
Serial Communications	The handling of data bits, one item after another. In serial communications each character (a byte) is broken into its component bits which are sent one at a time to a receiving device where they are re-assembled. Serial cables can span greater distances than those used for parallel.

Serial Port	The socket on a computer that allows serial communications to take place in and out of it. As the computer internally communicates in parallel, the serial port converts from one to the other both ways as well.
Server	A computer on a network that provides services for workstations. Often regarded as a "controlling computer", it can be dedicated (used as a server only) or non-dedicated (used as a workstation as well).
Session Layer	The fifth layer of the OSI model which dictates the conditions under which individual nodes on a network can communicate with each other.
SFSG	So Far So Good.
SIG	*Special Interest Group*. An ongoing discussion group in a Bulletin Board.
Signal	The process used to convey information, which could take the form of a voltage or a current waveform, a pulse of light or a radio wave. It could also mean a very short message, such as "Control Signal".
Signal to Noise Ratio	The proportion of noise within a signal.
Signon	Most communications services demand that you sign on at the start of a session with a string of characters that are unique to you—your identification, in other words.
Simplex	Either a circuit used in one direction only or one used in either direction but not at the same time, depending on whose definition you use. The latter is sometimes also called Half Duplex, again depending on the definition.
SITD	Still In The Dark.

SMB   *Server Message Block*. Yet another network protocol used by many manufacturers that allows one computer to use the files and peripherals of another as if they were locally available. This one was developed by Microsoft.

SMDS   *Switched Multimegabit Data Service*.

SNA   *System Network Architecture*. IBM's idea of a communications system which forms part of SAA, in association with SDLC, commonly used for transmitting data between an IBM host computer and a 3274 or 3276 controller.

SNAFU   Situation Normal - All Fouled Up.

SNMP   *Simple Network Management Protocol*. A control and reporting scheme for managing devices on a network.

SOBOH   Slap On Back Of Head.

SOH   *Start of Header*.

Space   The alternative condition of a line to Mark.

SONET   *S*ynchronous *O*ptical *NET*work.

SOTA   State Of The Art.

SPOOL   *Simultaneous Peripheral Operation On Line*, meaning the capability for two operations to happen at once. A spooler will take data addressed to the printer and store it until the printer is ready; then it will release it at a rate that is comfortable with the printer's speed (the same could apply with modems and communications). This saves you hanging around if there's a queue for the printer and allows you to do something else at the same time.

SPX   *Sequenced packet eXchange*. IPX, but with guaranteed delivery.

SQL	*Structured Query Language*. A language for data manipulation that is independent of the device or database in use, particularly useful in networking because a database loads only those records which match the query of the moment into the workstation. Traditional databases must be loaded completely into the local station memory in order for a search to take place, which increases traffic.
SSWL	Splits Sides With Laughter.
Star	A LAN topology where cables radiate from a central network processor. One workstation is attached to each cable.
StarLAN	A networking system developed by AT&T that uses CSMA protocols on twisted pair telephone wire.
Start Bit	In asynchronous transmissions, the bit sent before the first bit of a digital word. The start bit is always on. Its presence informs the receiving station of the coming data.
Start-Stop Transmission	Another name for *asynchronous transmission*.
STB	Simply The Best.
Stop Bit	A bit (or bits) placed at the end of a byte to indicate the end of transmitted data. There are sometimes more than one, such as 1.5 or 2.
Store and Forward	The handling of messages or packets in a network by accepting them completely into storage before sending them forward. Used as a method of concentrating lines without congestion.
STP	*Shielded Twisted Pair*. UTP with shielding.
STX	*Start of Transmission*.
SVC	*Switched Virtual Circuit*.

SWMBO   She Who Must Be Obeyed.

SWYM   See What You Mean.

SYN   Synchronisation.

Synchronous   A form of communication between devices where both ends of the transmission are locked in step from the beginning to the end of the session; a common time base is continually acted upon by the sender and receiver as the modems pulse in time with each other. The devices operate at substantially the same frequency and are maintained in a correct relationship by constant monitoring and adjustment for circuit conditions. As the meaning of each bit is dependent on its time of arrival, framing and error checking bits are unnecessary, so the data throughput rate is faster than it would be with asynchronous.

SysOp   *Sys*tem *Op*erator. The person in charge of running a Bulletin Board.

TAIISAT   Take An Interest In Sex And Travel. In other words, GO AWAY!

TANJ   There Aint No Justice.

TANSTAAFL   There Ain't No Such Thing As A Free Lunch.

TBW   That Blasted Woman.

TCP/IP   *Transmission Control Program/Internet Program*. A set of protocols originally developed by the Department of Defense in the USA to link dissimilar computers across large networks.

Transmission Control Protocol is used to establish communications between stations on a network by defining the kinds of messages they send and how they are acknowledged.

IP sets standards on how packets are made up, moved and addressed. Due to it being an industry standard (in the US, anyway), some manufacturers offer it as an option. It is extremely useful where dissimilar computers need to be conected.

TDM *Time Division Multiplexing.* A multiplexing method in which the time on the channel is allocated in turn to different subchannels and the data packets are interleaved with one another. The allocation may be regular in a fixed cycle or frame, or varied according to the needs of the subchannels.

Teletext The transmission of coded digital information as part of a television signal (it uses the blank bits), which can be decoded and displayed as text and graphics on a special receiver.

Teletype This term used loosely to describe keyboard/printer terminals. It's actually a trademark of *Teletype Corporation*, whose terminals were so successful that their specifications became a widely adopted standard. When a computer acts as a terminal to a remote host, Teletype is one of the emulations available.

Telex Network A switched public network with teleprinters as terminals.

Terminator A resistor used at both ends of an Ethernet cable to ensure that signals do not reflect back along the cable and cause errors.

TFTR Thanks For The Report.

TG Thank God.

Thick Ethernet A cabling system that uses large diameter coax to connect computers through transceivers.

Thin Ethernet Sometimes known as *Cheapernet*, as for Thick Ethernet, but with thinner and more flexible coax, with transceivers on the NIC.

TIA	*Telecommunications Industries Association*/Thanks In Anticipation.
TIC	Tongue In Cheek.
Timeouts	Timeouts bring into operation a predetermined event if another expected event does not occur in a set period. For instance, a timeout set for 6 seconds will cause a modem to hang up if nothing is heard on the telephone for that time.
Timesharing	The sharing of a resource between several users by giving each of them access (a time slot) in succession.
TIU	*Terminal Interface Unit.*
TLA	Three-Letter Acronym.
TMAI	Tell Me About It.
TMRTB	That Man Reads The Beano.
TNG	The Next Generation.
Token Passing	An access protocol in which a special packet (or token) circulates around a network giving stations permission to transmit when the token is in their possession. Any station wishing to transmit captures the token by setting a bit on it. When the transmission is completed, the station releases the token (and its hold on the network) by resetting the bit to free status.
Token Ring	A network scheme where packets are relayed around a ring.
Tone Dialling	See *MFT Dialling*.
TOP	*Technical Office Protocol*. Usually found living with MAP and uses CSMA and X400 standards.

Topology	Of networks, the physical layout of the nodes, terminals and lines; in other words, the map. Strictly, the pattern of connection (i.e. star), but the word also includes distance and geography. Common topologies include Bus, Tree, Ring, Star and Mesh.
T-Piece	Or T-connector, used to join two coaxial cables with a spur at rightangles that connects to the NIC.
TPTB	The Powers That Be.
Traffic	The volume of messages sent round a system. The term is often used as a rough measure of how much a system is used, such as light, medium or heavy.
Transceiver	A device capable of sending and receiving information. Commonly used externally on a Thick Ethernet network, but often incorporated on a network interface card for Thin Ethernet.
Transient Program	A program that releases the memory space occupied by it after executing its functions. This is as opposed to a *memory resident* one which remains in memory.
Transparent	Any process not noticeable to the user during normal operations.
Transport Layer	The fourth layer of the OSI model which checks the integrity of and formats the data carried by the physical layer, managed by the data layer and routed by the network layer, if implemented.
Transport Protocol	The basic level of protocol concerned with the transport of messages.
Trellis Coded Modulation	A form of coding that adds an extra bit to the data flow to create a predictable pattern. Receiving equipment is able to guess what should have been sent from the pattern changes. It doesn't correct errors but helps make data less susceptible to them. It's a standard feature of V.32*bis*.

TTBOMK	To The Best of My Knowledge.
TTFN	Ta Ta For Now.
TTFS	Try This For Size.
TTY	*TeleTYpe*. The most basic kind of terminal there is.
TTYL	Talk To You Later.
TVM	Ta Very Much.
TVMIA	Ta Very Much In Advance.
Twisted Pair Wiring	Cable consisting of two wires twisted together (6 turns per inch) which provides self-shielding, as the twisting tends to cancel out certain forms of interference. Some telephone wire is twisted pair.
TWMTBACT	That Was Meant To Be A Comment To...
TWSTBACT	That Was Supposed To Be A Comment To...
TXD	*Transmit Data*.
TYVM	Thank You Very Much.
UA	Unusual Abbreviation.
UART	*Universal Asynchronous Receiver/Transmitter*. The gadget that converts data transmission from parallel inside the computer to serial for the serial ports.
	On a single-tasking computer the original 8250/16450 design was enough, but something more powerful is needed these days. The 16550A is a pin-compatible replacement which contains twin 16-byte buffers that can hold data until the CPU is ready to process it (the original 16550 had a bug in it, hence the improved A version).
Uplink	A communications path from an Earth station to a satellite.

UPS	*Uninterruptible Power Supply.*
User	You.
UTCCH	Until The Cows Come Home.
UTP	See *Twisted Pair Wiring.*
UYMF	Up Yours, My Friend.
VC	See *Virtual Circuit.*
VGI	Very Good Idea.
Viewdata	Teletext-based service for accessing services through the telephone network.
Virtual Circuit	A concept used in X.25 to describe a notional circuit that is only in effect for the duration of a call, as when you use a telephone. Switched VCs allow a connection on a per-call basis, so they don't always connect the same two DTEs. Permanent VCs always connect two particular DTEs.
Volume	An area of a hard disk separated from other parts, typically used with NetWare.
VPL	Visible Panty Line.
V-Series	Recommendations for data transmission using the telephone network, thus many of them deal with modems. The best known is V.24, which lists the interchange circuits between a modem and its Data Terminal Equipment. Others include V.21, which covers 300 baud full duplex communication between modems and V.22*bis* which deals with 2400 baud.
VTP	*Virtual Terminal Protocol.*
WAGI	What A Good Idea.
WAIDW	What Am I Doing Wrong.
WASHITO	Wait And See How It Turns Out.

Wavelength Multiplexing	Used in optical fibres, where more than one wavelength of light is used to multiplex signal on to a fibre.
WFAC	Waiting For A Call.
WFMOB	Well Seduce My Ancient Footware.
WHYD	What Have You Done
WIBNI	Wouldn't It Be Nice If.
Wide Area Network	Combinations of equipment linked over a wide area, often by the telephone system.
Wideband	Communications channels having a wider bandwidth than that used for normal speech circuits, with very high speed transmission (typically 48 kbits/sec) which enables many high-speed data transfers to take place.
WIHIH	What in Hell is Happening?
WIMP	*Windows, Icons, Menus, Pulldowns*.
WIWAB	When I Was A Boy.
WIWAL	When I Were A Lad.
Workgroup	A subdivision of a larger network, formed for administrative convenience.
WRT	With Respect To.
WTBC	Wont That Be Confusing?
WTF	What The Hell.
WUASTC	Wake Up And Smell The Coffee.
WWFFC	Why Wait For Father Christmas
WWW	*World Wide Web*.
X-Series	CCITT recommendations for packet switching, such as X.25.

X.25	A standard that defines how data should be handled in a packet switched network.
X.400	CCITT standard dealing with electronic mail and message handling.
XModem	A simple send-and-wait protocol originally designed for the transmission of data between computers using the telephone system.
XNS	Distributed file system developed by Xerox.
XON/XOFF	A software handshaking system used for flow control.
YFST	Yawns For Some Time.
YHBM	You Have BinMail.
YHM	You Have Mail.
YHSM	You Have Snail Mail (i.e. normal post).
YKWIM	You Know What I Mean.
YOGWYPF	You Only Get What You Pay For.
YSBIB	You Should Be In Bed

Index